Developed and Published
by
AIMS Education Foundation

This book contains materials developed by the AIMS Education Foundation. **AIMS** (**A**ctivities **I**ntegrating **M**athematics and **S**cience) began in 1981 with a grant from the National Science Foundation. The non-profit AIMS Education Foundation publishes hands-on instructional materials that build conceptual understanding. The foundation also sponsors a national program of professional development through which educators may gain expertise in teaching math and science.

AIMS Education Foundation
P.O. Box 8120, Fresno, CA 93747-8120 • 888.733.2467 • aimsedu.org

ISBN 978-1-60519-036-5

Printed in the United States of America

I Hear and I Forget,

I See and I Remember,

I Do and I Understand.

-Chinese Proverb

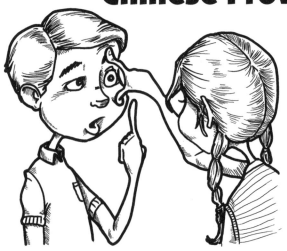

Table of Contents

The rubber band books offer valuable content information presented in a kid-friendly way. Each student can be given his or her own book to keep and refer to at a later date. These books also provide a great home link, as students can take them home and share the information they are learning with their parents.

To assemble a book, follow these simple instructions:

A #19 rubber band fits perfectly. If these are not available, clip off the inside corners of the book so that the other rubber bands can fit.

Urinary System

Digestive System

Respiratory System

Circulatory System

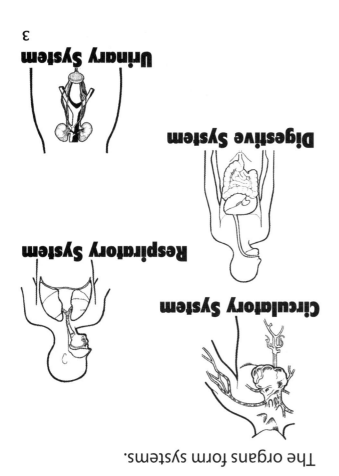

The organs form systems.

Skin

Liver

Heart

Lungs

These cells form tissues. The tissues form organs.

Human Cell

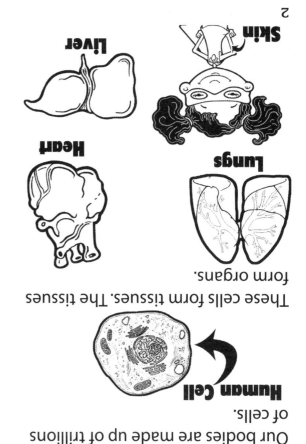

Our bodies are made up of trillions of cells.

Everything works together to allow us to live, reproduce, and interact with others and our environment. We are marvels!

Our Amazing Bodies

What is so amazing about our bodies?

FROM HEAD TO TOE

A Mind of Your Own

I think, therefore, I am.

Topic
Brain

Key Question
What are the main parts of your brain and their functions?

Learning Goals
Students will:
- read about the functions of various parts of the brain, and
- color and label a diagram of the brain with the names of the parts and their functions.

Guiding Documents
Project 2061 Benchmark
- *The brain gets signals from all parts of the body telling what is going on there. The brain also sends signals to parts of the body to influence what they do.*

NRC Standard
- *The human organism has systems for digestion, respiration, reproduction, circulation, excretion, movement, control, and coordination, and for protection from disease. These systems interact with one another.*

Science
Life science
    human body
        brain

Integrated Processes
Observing
Comparing and contrasting
Recording
Identifying

Materials
A Mind of Your Own rubber band book
#19 rubber bands
Transparent tape
Scissors
4" x 6" cards, one per student
Rulers
Colored pencils
Brain labels (see *Management 1*)
Brain diagram

Background Information
The human brain is a wonderfully complex organ that is responsible for regulating the body's functions, interpreting sensory information, thinking and reasoning, emotions, and more. Different parts of the brain are responsible for different functions. The included rubber band book provides the background information for the parts of the brain that will be studied in this activity.

Management
1. Copy the page of labels and the brain diagram page on card stock. Each student needs one set of six labels and one brain diagram. (Three sets of labels are printed on one page.)
2. Be sure the rulers have markings in inches.

Procedure
1. Ask students if they know the names of any of the parts of their brains. Record any responses on the board.
2. Explain that students will be learning more about the brain's structure and function.
3. Distribute the rubber band book and rubber bands. When students have assembled their books, read through the content together as a class.
4. Discuss the terms and clarify any points of confusion. Compare what they learned in the book to what they already knew about the brain.
5. Distribute the brain diagram page and colored pencils to each student. Invite students to color each part of the brain a different color, using the illustrations from the rubber band book as a guide.
6. When students are done coloring, distribute scissors, tape, and one set of labels to each student. Explain that they are to cut apart the labels and tape them to the page in the correct locations. They must be careful to tape them only on the sides and bottom so that each label makes a pocket that is open at the top.
7. When students have finished taping their labels in place, distribute a ruler and a 4" x 6" card to each student. Instruct them to measure and draw lines that divide the card into six squares that measure two inches on each side. Have them cut along these lines to get six squares.

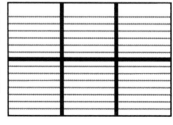

7

8. Explain that students will write the main functions of each of the parts of the brain on their small squares of paper. These pieces of paper will then be placed in the corresponding pockets on the diagram page.
9. When students are done, have them remove the cards from their pockets and trade cards and pages with another student. Challenge them to put their classmates' cards in the correct pockets without looking at the rubber band book. Check for accuracy and discuss what students learned.

Connecting Learning

1. What are some parts of the brain that you have heard of before?
2. How did the parts of the brain that we had already heard of compare to those we read about in the book?
3. What is the largest part of the brain? [cerebrum]
4. Which part of the brain has the most neurons? [cerebellum]
5. If someone had a brain injury that affected the cerebellum, what results might be expected? [loss of balance and coordination, having to re-learn tasks, etc.]
6. Which part of the brain controls our involuntary muscles—those things that we don't have control over? [brain stem]
7. Which part of the brain could be called the body's "thermostat"? [hypothalamus]
8. What are you wondering now?

Extensions

1. Do additional research on the brain and the functions of specific parts of the brain. (See *Internet Connections* for suggested websites.)
2. Find the specific parts of the brain that correspond to certain functions, such as sight and speech.

Internet Connections

KidsHealth®
http://kidshealth.org/kid/htbw/
Select the brain from the scrolling list for information on the brain and nervous system, diagrams, movies, and more.

Neuroscience for Kids
http://faculty.washington.edu/chudler/introb.html
Neuroscience information is organized by specific topics in chapters on the world of neuroscience, brain basics, the nervous system, neurons, and more.

Solutions

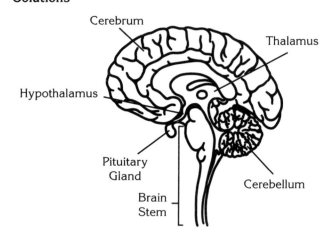

A Mind of Your Own

I think, therefore, I am.

Key Question

What are the main parts of your brain and their functions?

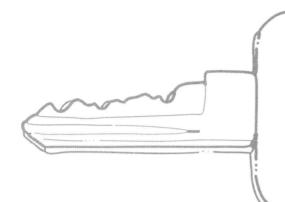

Learning Goals

Students will:

- read about the functions of various parts of the brain, and

- color and label a diagram of the brain with the names of the parts and their functions.

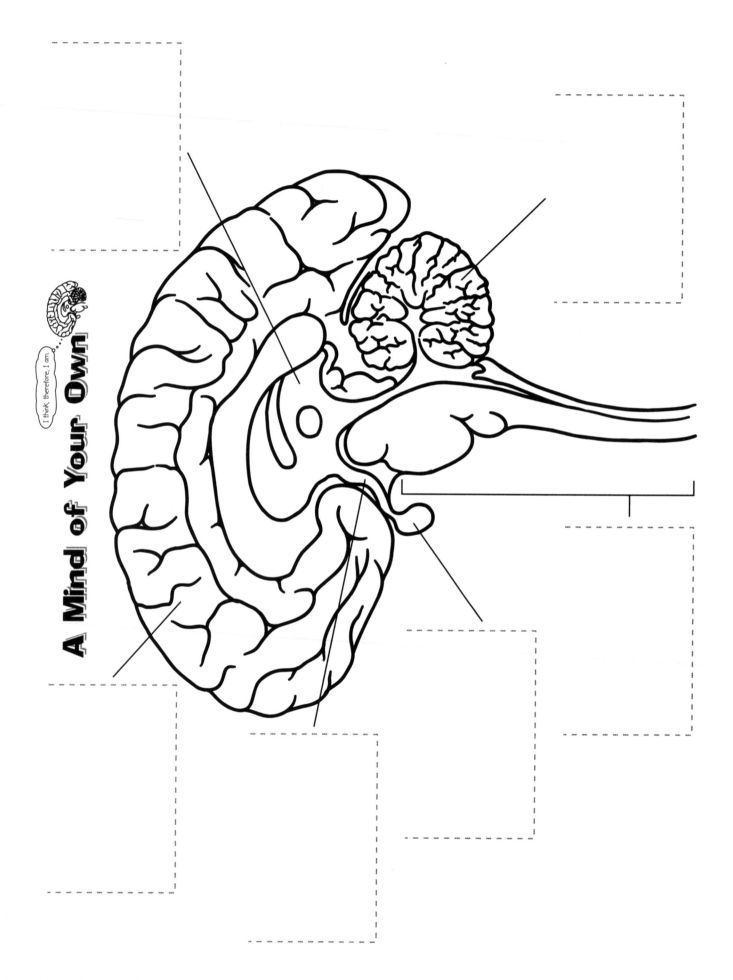

A Mind of Your Own

I think, therefore, I am.

Hypothalamus	**Cerebrum**	**Cerebellum**
Thalamus	**Pituitary Gland**	**Brain Stem**
Hypothalamus	**Cerebrum**	**Cerebellum**
Thalamus	**Pituitary Gland**	**Brain Stem**
Hypothalamus	**Cerebrum**	**Cerebellum**
Thalamus	**Pituitary Gland**	**Brain Stem**

The pituitary gland is another very small part of your brain. It sits just below the hypothalamus. It is responsible for releasing hormones to your body.

These hormones control:
- metabolism
- growth
- puberty
- water and mineral balance

Long ago people thought that the heart was the body part that was responsible for thoughts, memories, and emotions. Now we know that all of that—and much more—comes from the brain.

It is my belief that the heart is the center of thought, of emotion, of...

Even with all that we know about the brain, there is still much we don't know. Scientists are constantly doing research to learn more about our brains and how they work.

A Mind of Your Own

The thalamus is in the center of your brain. It receives sensory information (smell, sight, sound, etc.) from your body and sends it on to the cerebrum. The cerebrum also sends messages to the thalamus for it to send to other parts of the brain and spinal cord.

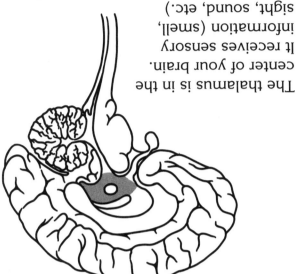

There are many parts to your brain that all work together with the rest of your body. The different parts have different jobs to do.

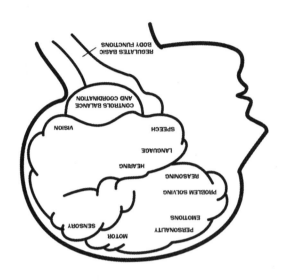

REGULATES BASIC BODY FUNCTIONS

CONTROLS BALANCE AND COORDINATION

VISION

SPEECH

LANGUAGE

HEARING

REASONING

PROBLEM SOLVING

EMOTIONS

PERSONALITY

SENSORY

MOTOR

One of the smallest parts of your brain is called the hypothalamus. It is about the size of a pea. It is in the middle of your brain in front of the thalamus and above the brain stem. One of its jobs is to control your body's temperature. It also regulates the pituitary gland, thirst, hunger, and sleep patterns.

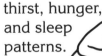

Your brain is the control center of your body. It is in charge of everything you do. You can use your brain to make certain things happen, like walking and talking. Other things, like interpreting signals from your eyes and making your heart beat, your brain does without any thought on your part.

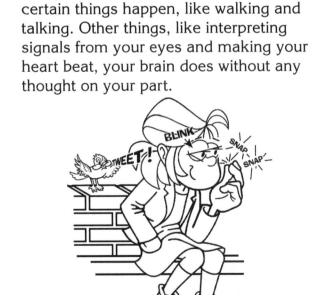

The cerebellum is much smaller than the cerebrum. Its name means "little brain." It is only about 10% of your brain, but it has more than 50% of the brain's neurons. It is at the back of your brain under the cerebrum.

The cerebellum controls:
- balance and posture
- movement and coordination
- motor learning (learning to ride a bike, hit a baseball, etc.)

Your cerebrum has two halves, called hemispheres. It is in charge of lots of things, including:
- speech
- memory
- thinking and reasoning
- voluntary muscles (the ones you can control)
- sensory processing (vision, hearing, touch, etc.)

Your brain stem connects your brain to your spinal cord. It is under the cerebrum and in front of the cerebellum. It is in charge of the things that keep you alive like:
- breathing
- digestion
- blood circulation

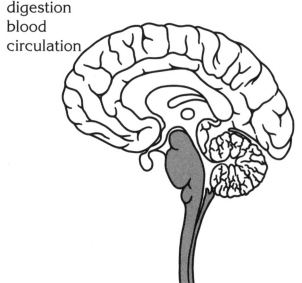

The biggest part of your brain is called the cerebrum. It makes up about 85% of your brain. When you see pictures or models of the brain, most of what you can see is the cerebrum.

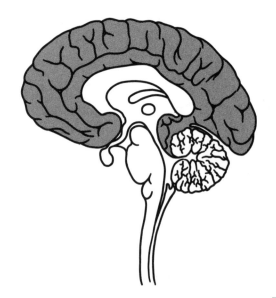

A Mind of Your Own

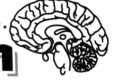

I think, therefore, I am.

Connecting Learning

1. What are some parts of the brain that you have heard of before?

2. How did the parts of the brain that we had already heard of compare to those we read about in the book?

3. What is the largest part of the brain?

4. Which part of the brain has the most neurons?

5. If someone had a brain injury that affected the cerebellum, what results might be expected?

A Mind of Your Own

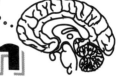

Connecting Learning

6. Which part of the brain controls our involuntary muscles—those things that we don't have control over?

7. Which part of the brain could be called the body's "thermostat"?

8. What are you wondering now?

Motor neurons take messages from the central nervous system to muscles and glands. When you walk, ride a bike, or turn a page, your motor neurons are at work.

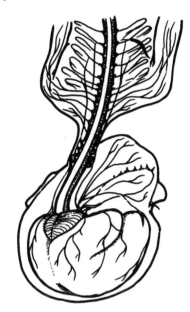

The central nervous system includes your brain and spinal cord. The brain is the control center of the body. It keeps all your parts working together as they should.

When your nervous system is working as it should, you don't even notice. But, there are some diseases that affect the nervous system. Epilepsy, multiple sclerosis, and Parkinson's disease are all caused by problems in the nervous system.

The Nervous System

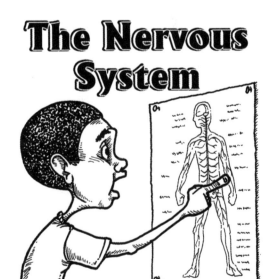

Your brain, spinal cord, and nerves form the nervous system. The nervous system is divided into two parts:
- the central nervous system, and
- the peripheral nervous system.

Autonomic nerve fibers carry messages from the central nervous system to the body's organs and glands. Keeping the heart beating or the stomach digesting are functions of the autonomic nerves.

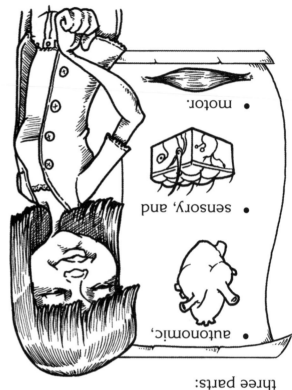

The peripheral nervous system has three parts:

- autonomic,
- sensory, and
- motor.

Sensory nerves take messages from sensory receptors to the central nervous system. When you eat something, the sensory nerves carry the message from the receptors in your tongue to your brain so you can experience taste.

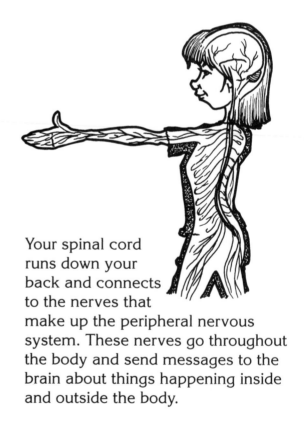

Your spinal cord runs down your back and connects to the nerves that make up the peripheral nervous system. These nerves go throughout the body and send messages to the brain about things happening inside and outside the body.

You've Got Some Nerve

Topic
Nervous system

Key Question
How can we model the method the brain uses to send and receive messages to and from parts of the body?

Learning Goal
Students will play a relay game to model the way the brain sends and receives signals to and from various parts of the body.

Guiding Documents
Project 2061 Benchmarks
- *The brain gets signals from all parts of the body telling what is going on there. The brain also sends signals to parts of the body to influence what they do.*
- *Models are often used to think about processes that happen too slowly, too quickly, or on too small a scale to observe directly, or that are too vast to be changed deliberately, or that are potentially dangerous.*

NRC Standard
- *The human organism has systems for digestion, respiration, reproduction, circulation, excretion, movement, control, and coordination, and for protection from disease. These systems interact with one another.*

Science
Life science
    human body
        brain
        nervous system

Integrated Processes
Observing
Comparing and contrasting
Relating

Materials
You've Got Some Nerve rubber band book
#19 rubber bands
Wooden cube or die (see *Management 2*)
3" x 5" cards (see *Management 3*)

Background Information
The brain is the control center of the body. All thoughts, movements, emotions, physiological responses, and reflexes come from or are controlled by the brain. The brain accomplishes all of this with the help of the nervous system, which, along with the brain, includes the spinal cord and nerves. Nerve cells, called neurons, transmit messages to and from the brain and various parts of the body.

Neurons are specialized cells that transmit messages by means of an electrochemical process. While they contain many of the same parts as other cells in the body (nucleus, cytoplasm, mitochondria, etc.), they have specialized structures that are unique to neurons. Dendrites and axons are specialized extensions that allow neurons to communicate with each other. Dendrites carry information into the cell, and axons carry it away from the cell.

Different neurons have different functions. Sensory neurons send information to the brain from the sensory receptors found in the eyes, ears, nose, mouth, and skin. Motor neurons transmit information from the brain to muscles or glands. Interneurons send messages between sensory and motor neurons.

This activity will model the transmission of messages from the brain to various body parts by having students participate in a "neuron relay." They will transmit a message by squeezing hands down a row to represent the communication between neurons that occurs when the brain sends messages to the body.

Management
1. Students must be divided into two groups with the same number of people. If you have an even number of students, select two to help you referee the relay and keep score. If you have an odd number, one student can provide the assistance.
2. Use sticky dots or masking tape to cover the faces of a die that read four, five, and six. Draw one, two, and three dots on these covered faces so that the die has only ones, twos, and threes. You can also use a permanent marker to write numbers on the faces of a wooden cube.
3. Write each number from one to three on a 3" x 5" index card.
4. You will need an open area in which the teams of students can make two lines of chairs that are back to back. At each end of the lines of chairs, place

another chair, low table, or stool. The die will go on the extra chair at one end, and the three index cards will go on the extra chair at the other end.

Procedure

1. Ask students what they already know about the brain and how it sends and receives messages to and from various parts of the body.
2. Distribute the rubber band book and read through it as a class. Discuss the way neurons work and clarify any terms or concepts with which students are having difficulty.
3. Explain that students are going to be participating in an activity that will model how the brain sends messages through the neurons to parts of the body. Divide the class into two groups, keeping either one or two students to be your assistant(s).
4. Have the class take their chairs to an open area and form two lines with their chairs so that the two teams are sitting back to back. Place the chair with the die at one end of the line and the chair with the three index cards at the other end of the line.
5. Once students are seated, explain that the student in the chair closest to the die represents the brain. The students in the middle of the line represent the neurons along the path from the brain to the hand, and the student at the end farthest from the die represents the hand.
6. Tell students that they will be having a little friendly competition to see which team has the fastest nervous system. The challenge is to get a specific message from the brain to the hand as quickly as possible. The assistant(s) will be refereeing and keeping score. The message will be transmitted from the "brain" to the "hand" by students squeezing their hands a certain number of times in sequence down the row.
7. Explain that you (or one of the assistants) will roll the die and that the number will be either a one, a two, or a three. As soon as the number is rolled, the "brain" must squeeze the hand of the person sitting next to him/her that number of times. That person must squeeze the hand of the person sitting on his/her other side the same number of times and so on down the line until the message reaches the "hand." The "hand" must grab the index card that corresponds to the number of times his/her hand was squeezed. Because there is only one index card with each number, the first team to grab the correct index card will get a point. The index card is returned to the chair, and the die will be rolled again. The first team to reach five points will be declared the body with the fastest nervous system.

8. Emphasize that there is to be no talking during this relay. The only person who is allowed to look at the die is the brain; all other students must be facing the chair with the index cards. Students are to do nothing until they receive a signal from the person sitting next to them, at which point they pass the signal on as quickly as they can.
9. Play the game several times allowing different students to be the "brain" and the "hand." Compare results and discuss how this relay models what is happening in your body when messages are sent to and from the brain.

Connecting Learning

1. How does your brain send and receive messages to and from the body?
2. What are some of the kinds of neurons we have in our bodies? [sensory, motor, interneurons]
3. Which kind of neurons were we modeling in this activity? [motor] How do you know? [Motor neurons send messages from the brain to muscles and other parts of the body.]
4. How was our relay like what actually happens in our bodies when messages are sent to and from the brain? [Messages are sent from neuron to neuron, just like we sent them from person to person.] How was it different? [Neurons transmit messages much more quickly, neurons use an electrochemical process to transmit messages, etc.]
5. Did your team get faster the longer you played? Explain.
6. Did changing the people who were the "brain" and the "hand" make a difference in response time? Explain.
7. Which message (number) was easiest to relay? ...most difficult? Why?
8. What are you wondering now?

You've Got Some Nerve

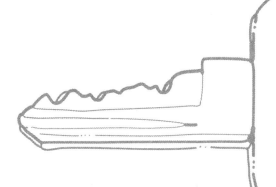

Key Question

How can we model the method the brain uses to send and receive messages to and from parts of the body?

Learning Goal

play a relay game to model the the brain sends and receives signals to and from various parts of the body.

Dendrites take information from another neuron and bring it in to the cell. Axons send information from the neuron out to other neurons. This information is sent by a special electrochemical process.

Uh-oh ! I knew I should have switched off that circuit breaker ffft!

2

These messages allow you to do everything from breathing to walking to talking to seeing. The question is, how do these messages get to and from the brain?

OUCH !! *Stove really IS hot !*

To: Cory's Brain
Neural Pathway #247
Topotheneck, Cerebrum

From: Cory's Right Hand
Endoforearm
Fingertips and Palm

Your neurons help keep your body working just as it should. Next time you blink or take a breath or open your mouth to speak, think about all of the neurons involved that made it happen.

SNAP SNAP BLINK BLINK

You've Got Some Nerve

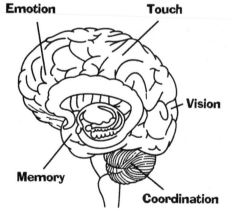

Emotion · Touch · Vision · Memory · Coordination

As you know, your brain is the control center of the body. It works with the other parts of the nervous system to send messages to parts of your body. It also receives messages from parts of your body and interprets them.

8

1

neurons.

Different kinds of neurons have different jobs. Some take messages to the brain from your sensory receptors (in eyes, ears, nose, etc). These are called sensory neurons.

Others take information from the brain to muscles or other body parts. These are called motor neurons. A third kind of neuron sends messages between motor neurons and sensory neurons. These are called interneurons.

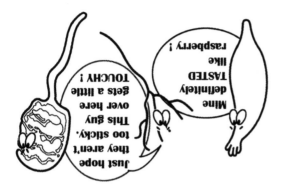

5

4

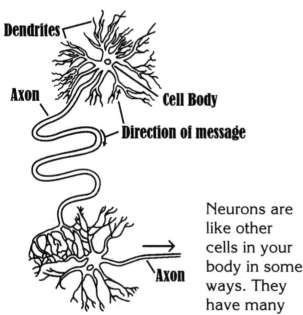

Dendrites

Axon

Cell Body

Direction of message

Axon

Neurons are like other cells in your body in some ways. They have many of the same parts. But, they have two special parts that other cells don't have. These parts let them send and receive messages. They are called the dendrites and the axons.

The answer is the nerves, or neurons to be exact. Neurons are special nerve cells in your body. You are born with billions of neurons. Most of these neurons are in your brain and spinal cord.

6

3

You've Got Some Nerve

Connecting Learning

1. How does your brain send and receive messages to and from the body?

2. What are some of the kinds of neurons we have in our bodies?

3. Which kind of neurons were we modeling in this activity? How do you know?

4. How was our relay like what actually happens in our bodies when messages are sent to and from the brain? How was it different?

5. Did your team get faster the longer you played? Explain.

You've Got Some Nerve

Connecting Learning

6. Did changing the people who were the "brain" and the "hand" make a difference in response time? Explain.

7. Which message (number) was easiest to relay? ...most difficult? Why?

8. What are you wondering now?

A Heart-felt Model

Topic
Human heart

Key Question
How is our heart model like the human heart?

Learning Goals
Students will:
• learn about the structure and function of the human heart,
• construct a working model of the human heart, and
• compare the model to the real heart.

Guiding Documents
Project 2061 Benchmarks
• *Like other animals, human beings have body systems for obtaining and providing energy, defense, reproduction, and the coordination of body functions.*
• *To burn food for the release of energy stored in it, oxygen must be supplied to cells, and carbon dioxide removed. Lungs take in oxygen for the combustion of food and they eliminate the carbon dioxide produced. The urinary system disposes of dissolved waste molecules, the intestinal tract removes solid wastes, and the skin and lungs rid the body of heat energy. The circulatory system moves all these substances to or from cells where they are needed or produced, responding to changing demands.*
• *Models are often used to think about processes that happen too slowly, too quickly, or on too small a scale to observe directly, or that are too vast to be changed deliberately, or that are potentially dangerous.*

NRC Standards
• *Specialized cells perform specialized functions in multicellular organisms. Groups of specialized cells cooperate to form a tissue, such as a muscle. Different tissues are in turn grouped together to form larger functional units, called organs. Each type of cell, tissue, and organ has a distinct structure and set of functions that serve the organism as a whole.*
• *The human organism has systems for digestion, respiration, reproduction, circulation, excretion, movement, control, and coordination, and for protection from disease. These systems interact with one another.*

Science
Life science
    human body
        heart

Integrated Processes
Observing
Comparing and contrasting
Relating

Materials
For each group:
    two 20-ounce plastic bottles
    connector tube (see *Management 4*)
    metal washer, quarter inch
    two flexible plastic drinking straws
    scissors
    forceps
    nail with a sharp point
    pencil
    permanent marker
    construction instructions

For each student:
    A Heart-felt Model rubber band book
    #19 rubber band

For the class:
    5-minute epoxy or glue gun (see *Management 2*)

Background Information
The heart is a powerful muscle that continuously pumps oxygen and nutrients around the body. The heart contains two coordinated pumps and is divided into four chambers. Four one-way valves allow blood to flow through the four chambers in only one direction. When the body is at rest, it takes approximately one minute for blood to make a full circuit through the lungs and body.

In this activity, students will construct a two-chamber model heart. Something positive happens to your level of understanding of the heart as soon as you start pumping the colored water around the two-bottle model, and then comparing the operation of the model with the operation of a real heart. This model is quite different from a real heart, but it does demonstrate three important features of the real heart.

27

First, the colored water in the model is pumped around a closed loop. In the real heart, blood is also pumped around a closed loop.

Second, the action of the one-way valve in the model keeps the water flowing around the model in one direction. This is just like the four one-way valves in a real heart.

And third, at each beat of the heart, the heart takes in as much blood as it pumps out. This ensures that blood congestion does not occur. The level mark on the top bottle shows that the water level in the two chambers of the model also remains constant.

Constructing this working model of the heart can also lead one to think about the problems doctors and engineers had in designing and building AbioCor, the world's first fully implantable, mechanical, total heart replacement. The AbioCor is a one-kilogram electric-powered pump made of titanium and plastic. It is designed specifically for patients whose own hearts have been irreparably damaged. The mechanical heart is designed to give patients a new, although limited, lease on life.

How the model works

When the bottom bottle is squeezed, the increased pressure forces water up the plastic straw tube and into the top bottle. During this flow, the one-way valve stops water from going up through the bottle's neck into the top bottle (see *a* in diagram).

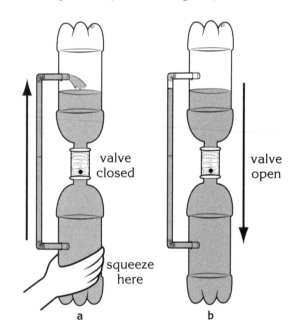

The water that flows into the top bottle then flows through the open one-way valve back into the bottom bottle (see *b*).

Management

1. Remove the labels from the plastic bottles before doing the activity. If necessary, use a commercial "goo" remover or lemon juice to remove the residue of glue left behind after removing the label. If a thin plastic ring is on the bottle's neck, remove it. The connector tube will fit tighter if this ring is removed.
2. If 5-minute epoxy is not available, use the cool-set glue guns. It is recommended that an adult be the one to seal the straws using either the epoxy or the glue gun.
3. If any part of the construction is too difficult for your students, you may want to have the components pre-made.
4. Connector tubes (item number 3100) and forceps (item number 3065) are available from AIMS.

Procedure

1. Ask students what they know about their hearts and how they work. Write some of the key words and vocabulary they come up with on the board.
2. Distribute the rubber band book to each student and read through it as a class. Compare what students already knew to what was in the book. Add any new information to the board and correct any things that were inaccurate.
3. Explain that students will be making a model of the heart and how it pumps blood. Unlike their hearts, this model will have only two chambers instead of four.
4. Divide students into groups and distribute the materials. Allow time for groups to construct and assemble the models. Have them come to you (or another adult) when they are ready for their straws to be sealed to the bottles.
5. After students have had time to explore their models, close with a time of class discussion.

Connecting Learning

1. How is the model heart like a real human heart? [has chambers, has a valve, liquid flows in a closed system, etc.] How is it different? [only two chambers, one valve, no body, etc.]
2. What function does the valve serve in the model? [It keeps the water from going the wrong way through the model.] How does this compare to what our valves do in our hearts? [The valves keep the blood from flowing in the wrong direction.]
3. Why are the left atrium and ventricle on the right side of the heart diagrams and the right atrium and ventricle on the left? [The diagrams show a view of the heart from the front. The left and right labels correspond to the left and right sides of the heart within the body.]

4. Where does blood first enter the heart? [It comes into the right atrium and passes through the one-way valve into the right ventricle.]
5. Where does the blood go once it has entered the right side of the heart? [through the pulmonary valve and out to the lungs]
6. What happens to the blood in the lungs? [The carbon dioxide in the blood is released into the lungs and exhaled, and the blood is reoxygenated.]
7. Where does the blood go from the lungs? [It reenters the heart on the left side, going into the left atrium, through the valve, and into the left ventrical.]
8. Where does the blood go once it has entered the left side of the heart? [through the aortic valve and out to the body]
9. Why is blood necessary for us to live? [It carries oxygen and nutrients throughout our bodies. It also carries our waste products like carbon dioxide to the lungs and other wastes to the urinary system so that the body can get rid of them.]
10. Explain why your heart couldn't survive without your lungs and your lungs couldn't survive without your heart.
11. What are you wondering now?

Internet Connections
KidsHealth®
http://kidshealth.org/kid/htbw/
Select the heart from the scrolling list for information on the heart and circulatory system, diagrams, movies, and more.

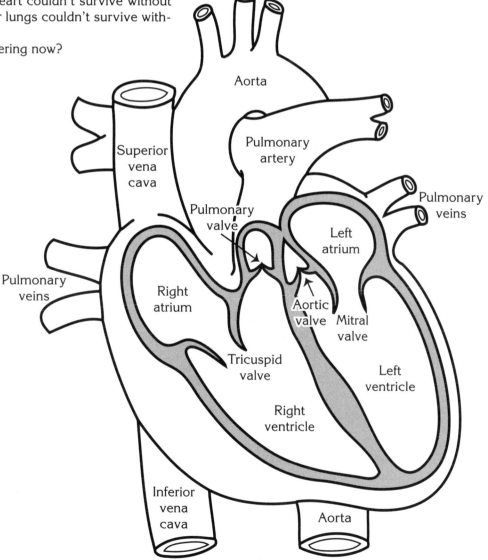

A Heart-felt Model

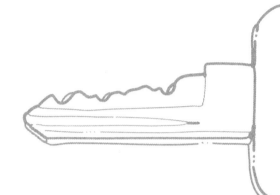

Key Question

How is our heart model like the human heart?

Learning Goals

Students will:

- learn about the structure and function of the human heart,

- construct a working model of the human heart, and

- compare the model to the real heart.

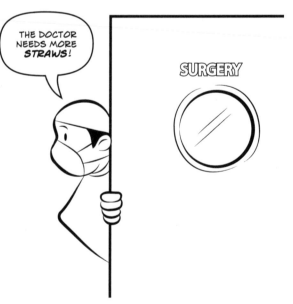

THE DOCTOR NEEDS MORE STRAWS!

SURGERY

The blood then passes through another one-way valve (4) and out of the heart to the left lung (5) and the right lung (6).

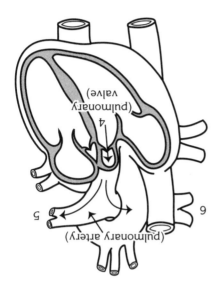

(pulmonary valve)
4
5
(pulmonary artery)
6

I GIVE YOU MY...
BRAIN?!?

LOVE MY

People used to think that the heart was the center of emotion. That's why we talk about broken hearts or giving people our hearts. We now know that emotion comes from the brain. So, what does the heart do?

The blood absorbs oxygen in the lungs and re-enters the heart (7 and 8) in the left atrium (c). From the left atrium, it passes through a one-way valve (9) to the left ventricle (d) and on out of the heart through the aorta to the head and arms (10) and the abdomen and legs (11). All of this happens about 60 times each minute!

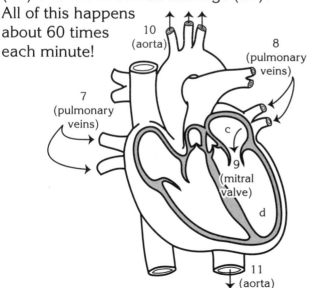

10 (aorta)
8 (pulmonary veins)
7 (pulmonary veins)
c
9 (mitral valve)
d
11 (aorta)

A Heart-felt Model

"COLD-HEARTED"   "BROKEN HEART"   "HEART-FELT"

"Have a heart!" "You broke my heart!" "That's so cold-hearted!" "That was a heart-felt response." You have probably heard phrases like these before. Maybe you've even used one yourself. We talk a lot about the heart, but what do you know about what your heart actually does?

The heart is divided into four parts, called chambers. Each side of the heart has two chambers—one on top and one on bottom. The chambers on top are called the atria (singular: atrium). You have a left atrium and a right atrium.

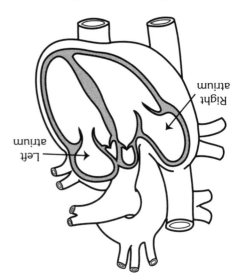

The chambers on bottom are called ventricles. You have a left ventricle and a right ventricle. These four chambers work together to move blood in and out of the heart. They are separated by one-way valves to keep blood moving in the right direction.

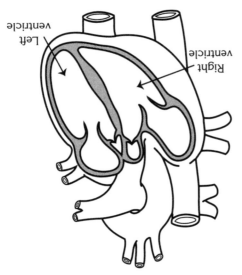

Blood coming from the body that is poor in oxygen enters the right atrium of the heart (a) through two main veins (1 and 2). From there it passes through a one-way valve (3) into the right ventricle (b).

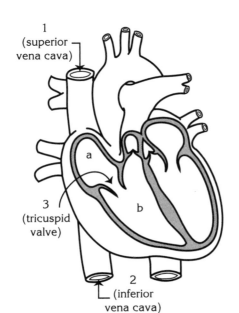

The heart is an organ made of muscle about the size of your fist. It works like a pump, sending blood around your body. Blood carries oxygen and nutrients to the body. It also carries away waste.

Making the One-Way Valve

1. Cut a two-inch strip of duct tape. Place the tape, sticky side up, on a flat surface.

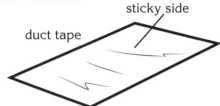

sticky side

duct tape

2. Fold over the tape but leave a portion of the sticky side—at least as wide as the width of the washer between its inner and outer diameters.

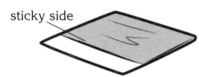

sticky side

3. Place the washer on the tape so that the inside diameter just reaches the sticky portion of the tape.

¼-inch washer

4. Use scissors to trim the tape from around the rim of the washer.

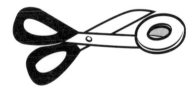

5. Turn the washer over. Bend the doubled part of the duct tape back to make a flap. This tape flap is the one-way valve used in the model.

 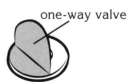

one-way valve

Constructing the Plastic Straw Connector

1. Bend up the short ends of the flexible straws.

flexible plastic straws

2. Use the tapered end of a ballpoint pen or pencil to flare the end of one of the flexible straws. Insert the pen into the straw and gently rotate it to produce the flared end.

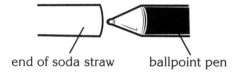

end of soda straw   ballpoint pen

3. Slide the end of the other flexible straw into the flared straw. Push to get a tight seal.

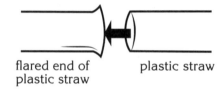

flared end of plastic straw   plastic straw

4. This straw connector will allow water to be pumped from the bottom bottle to the top bottle.

Installing the Valve in the Connector Tube

1. The center of the connector tube has a recessed area that surrounds the hole. The one-way valve will just fit into this recess. Peel the tape from the washer. Use a pair of forceps to place the valve, sticky side against the plastic lip of the recess, so that it covers the hole. Press the sticky part tightly against the lip of the recess.

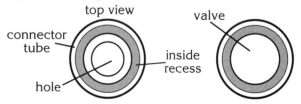

top view

connector tube

valve

inside recess

hole

Putting the Parts Together

1. Thread the connector tube onto one of the bottles. Thread the remaining bottle to the other end of the connector tube. Be sure both bottles are firmly seated in the tube. Mark the end of the connector tube that contains the one-way valve.

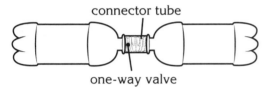

connector tube

one-way valve

2. Place the plastic straws against the connected bottles and mark the two points where the straws will be connected to the bottles.

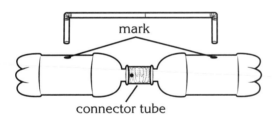

mark

connector tube

3. Use the end of a nail and carefully poke a small hole at the two marks on the bottle where the plastic straws will be connected to the bottles.

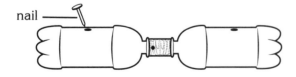

nail

4. Carefully use a sharpened pencil to enlarge the holes.

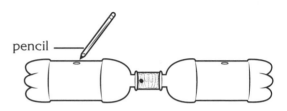

pencil

5. Attach the plastic straws to the bottles by slipping the ends of the straws through the holes in the sides of the bottles. Make sure the straws are still firmly connected. Take your model to your teacher so he or she can use glue to seal the straws to the bottles.

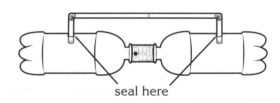

seal here

THE DOCTOR NEEDS MORE *STRAWS!*

SURGERY

A Heart-felt Model

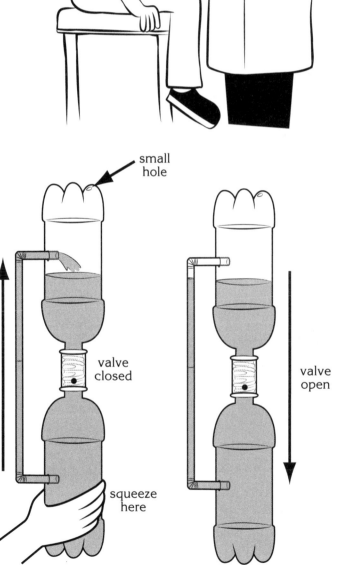

WE WERE ABLE TO SAVE SOME MONEY BY USING **HOUSEHOLD ITEMS** TO MAKE YOUR HEART.

YOUR HEART SURGERY BILL COMES TO **$5.32.**

Filling and Testing the Model

1. Turn the connected bottles so that they stand vertically with the one-way valve in the connector tube at the bottom.

2. Carefully disconnect the plastic drinking straws. Hold the connector tube tightly in one hand and unthread the top bottle.

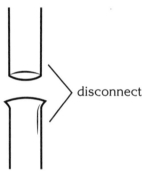

disconnect

3. Fill the bottom bottle with water. Use the nail to poke a small hole in the top bottle. Enlarge the hole with a pencil. Align the straws and thread the top bottle back onto the connector. When tight, the straws should be aligned. Connect the straws again and wrap them with a piece of transparent tape. Pour water through the small hole into the top bottle. Squeeze the bottom bottle and water should enter the straws and exit into the top bottle. Pump the bottom bottle several times to remove any air trapped in the plastic straws. Mark the water level in the upper bottle. Add a few drops of red food coloring through the top hole.

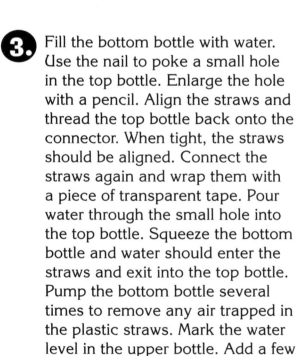

small hole

valve closed

squeeze here

valve open

Connecting Learning

1. How is the model heart like a real human heart? How is it different?

2. What function does the valve serve in the model? How does this compare to what our valves do in our hearts?

3. Why are the left atrium and ventricle on the right side of the heart diagrams and the right atrium and ventricle on the left?

4. Where does blood first enter the heart?

5. Where does the blood go once it has entered the right side of the heart?

Connecting Learning

6. What happens to the blood in the lungs?

7. Where does the blood go from the lungs?

8. Where does the blood go once it has entered the left side of the heart?

9. Why is blood necessary for us to live?

10. Explain why your heart couldn't survive without your lungs and your lungs couldn't survive without your heart.

11. What are you wondering now?

Heart Strings

Topic
Circulatory system

Key Questions
1. What are the components of the circulatory system?
2. What does the circulatory system transport?

Learning Goals
Students will:
- build a simplified model of the circulatory system,
- connect arteries to capillaries to veins, and
- understand that the blood gets oxygen from passing through the lungs and it leaves carbon dioxide in the lungs to be exhaled.

Guiding Documents

Project 2061 Benchmarks
- *Like other animals, human beings have body systems for obtaining and providing energy, defense, reproduction, and the coordination of body functions.*
- *To burn food for the release of energy stored in it, oxygen must be supplied to cells, and carbon dioxide removed. Lungs take in oxygen for the combustion of food and they eliminate the carbon dioxide produced. The urinary system disposes of dissolved waste molecules, the intestinal tract removes solid wastes, and the skin and lungs rid the body of heat energy. The circulatory system moves all these substances to or from cells where they are needed or produced, responding to changing demands.*
- *Models are often used to think about processes that happen too slowly, too quickly, or on too small a scale to observe directly, or that are too vast to be changed deliberately, or that are potentially dangerous.*

NRC Standards
- *Specialized cells perform specialized functions in multicellular organisms. Groups of specialized cells cooperate to form a tissue, such as a muscle. Different tissues are in turn grouped together to form larger functional units, called organs. Each type of cell, tissue, and organ has a distinct structure and set of functions that serve the organism as a whole.*
- *The human organism has systems for digestion, respiration, reproduction, circulation, excretion,*

movement, control, and coordination, and for protection from disease. These systems interact with one another.

Science
Life science
  human body
    circulatory system

Integrated Processes
Observing
Comparing and contrasting
Applying

Materials
Roving yarn, two colors (see *Management 1* and *2)*
Regular yarn, same two colors (see *Management 1* and *2)*
Crochet thread, one of the two colors (see *Management 1)*
Bulletin board paper (see *Management 3)*
Glue
Heart picture
Colored marker (see *Management 1)*
The Circulatory System rubber band book
#19 rubber bands

Background Information
The circulatory system is comprised of the heart, arteries (and arterioles), capillaries, and veins (and venules). The circulatory system is a closed system in which blood travels one way, thanks to the pump (the heart) and a series of valves that prevent the blood from going the wrong way.

The circulatory system is the means for transporting nutrients and oxygen to every part of the body. It is also the means for picking up wastes such as carbon dioxide and carrying them to the lungs, the liver, and the kidneys so the body can expel them. The blood also helps to regulate our temperature, pH balance, and water content. There are very few parts of the body that can function without dependence upon the circulatory system. Some are: fingernails, toenails, the dead outer layers of the skin and hair, the corneas of the eyes, and the enamel of the teeth.

The heart is a powerful muscle that continuously pumps blood to approximately 90,000 miles of blood vessels! The heart pumps blood into arteries that carry it away from the heart. The arteries have thick walls to withstand the pressure of the blood being pumped from the heart. As the arteries make their way from the heart, they branch off and become a network of increasingly fine arteries called arterioles finally ending in the smallest of all vessels, the capillaries. The capillaries become so thin that red blood cells have to pass through them in single file. The thinness of these capillaries allows the nutrients, gases, and wastes to pass through their walls. When the blood has exchanged its nutrients and oxygen for carbon dioxide and other wastes, it begins its journey back to the heart, first through the capillaries, then into the venules (fine veins) and finally into the veins.

To make a comparison of vessel sizes: the largest arteries and veins can be 2.5-3 cm in diameter, the smallest capillaries 0.0008 cm—that's about 3000 times smaller!

Management

1. The yarn needs to be in two different colors to represent arterial and venous blood. The crochet thread that represents capillaries should be in the color of the arterial blood, but students will use a marker of the same color as the venous blood to color in the second half of the capillary. This is the transition place of arterial to venous flow.

2. Be sure to dispel the idea that blood is blue. Textbook diagrams often use red illustrations to represent arterial flow and blue illustrations to represent venous flow. Also contributing to the blue-blood idea is that when students see the veins in their hands, they look blue. All normal blood is red.

3. Students will work in groups of four or five. They will need to have an outline of one of their bodies. Because this may cause management problems, ask a volunteer from each group to take the bulletin board paper home so that a parent or guardian can do the outline.

4. Roving yarn will be used to represent the largest arteries and veins, regular yarn will represent the arterioles and venules, and crochet thread will represent the capillaries.

5. It is not necessary that students try to put lots and lots of vessels in their body outlines. The big ideas you want students to know are the components of the circulatory system, how the circulatory system reaches all parts of the body, the interaction of the circulatory and respiratory system, and what the circulatory system transports.

Procedure

1. Ask the *Key Questions* and state the *Learning Goals*.
2. Have students get into groups of four or five. Tell them that they will be using the body outlines to display the circulatory system.
3. Distribute *The Circulatory System* rubber band book and #19 rubber bands. Give students time to read and discuss what they've read as a group and then to share pertinent points with the whole class.

4. Have students look at the illustration of the circulatory system. Ask what components they will need to include on their body pictures. [the heart, arteries, capillaries, and veins] Tell them that they will also draw in the lungs because the lungs must oxygenate the blood before it travels to other parts of the body.

5. Explain the yarn color system and tell students that they will make a key on the paper of the body outline. Discuss that the largest arteries and veins are closest to the heart and that for these the students will use the roving yarn.

6. Discuss the branching pattern that arteries, veins, and capillaries have and the fact that they are all connected. Tell students that they will be tying (or gluing) the regular yarn that represents smaller arteries (arterioles) and smaller veins (venules) to the roving yarn. Then to the regular yarn they will be tying (or gluing) the crochet thread.

7. Make certain that students understand that the capillaries (the crochet thread) connect the arterial system with the venous system. To show this, students will need to shade the one end of the capillary to match the veins.

8. Direct them to cut out the illustration of the heart and to glue it into place on the body outline. Encourage students to first sketch their blood vessel plan on their body outlines. Have them make their color keys. Tell them to use a marker to draw in the outlines of the lungs.

9. Invite them to get the roving yarn to begin gluing on their "heart strings." Tell them that they can get the yarn and crochet thread as needed.

10. When finished, have students display their outlines and discuss what they've learned.

Connecting Learning

1. What are the components of the circulatory system?
2. Compare and contrast the arteries, veins, and capillaries.
3. Why is the circulatory system important to us?
4. How do our lungs work with our circulatory system?
5. Why do you think our capillaries are so thin?
6. Has a doctor ever had to take blood from you to see why you were sick? If so, how did he or she take it?
7. What did you learn from this experience?
8. What are you wondering now?

Internet Connections

KidsHealth®
http://kidshealth.org/kid/htbw/
Select the heart from the scrolling list for information on the heart and circulatory system, diagrams, movies, and more.

Key Questions

1. What are the components of the circulatory system?

2. What does the circulatory system transport?

Learning Goals

- build a simplified model of the circulatory system,

- connect arteries to capillaries to veins, and

- understand that the blood gets oxygen from passing through the lungs and it leaves carbon dioxide in the lungs to be exhaled.

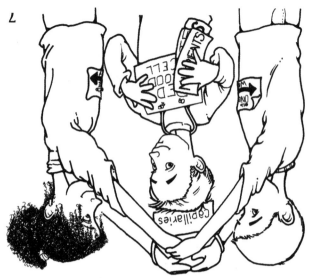

The capillaries become so thin that red blood cells have to pass through them in single file. The thinness of these capillaries allows the nutrients, gases, and wastes to pass through their walls. When the blood has exchanged its nutrients and oxygen for carbon dioxide and other wastes, it begins its journey back to the heart, first through the capillaries, then into the fine veins and finally into the larger veins.

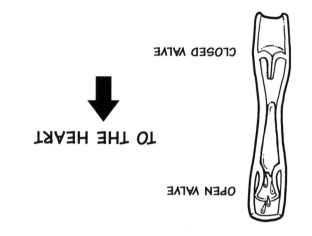

OPEN VALVE

TO THE HEART

CLOSED VALVE

The circulatory system is made up of the heart and a network of vessels known as the arteries, capillaries, and veins. It is a closed system in which blood travels one way, thanks to the pump (the heart) and a series of valves that prevent the blood from going the wrong way.

The veins don't have to have the thick walls like the arteries because they really have a low-pressure job. As a matter of fact, some veins have to have valves to prevent backflow—backing up is not allowed in this transport system!

The Circulatory System

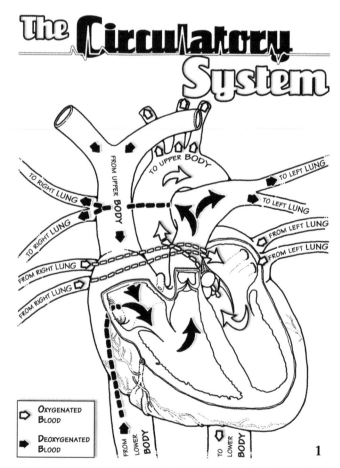

The heart is a powerful muscle that continuously pumps blood to about 90,000 miles of blood vessels! The heart pumps blood into arteries that carry it away from the heart.

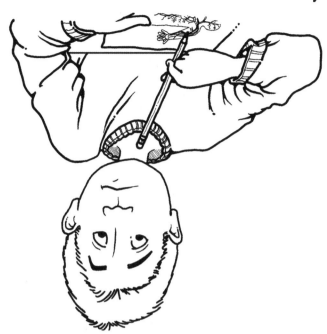

So why don't you see all these blood vessels on illustrations of the human circulatory system? Because there are too many to draw and some are much too small!

The arteries are the big guys of the vessel group. They have thick muscular walls that can take the pressure of the blood as it is forced out of the heart. As the arteries make their way from the heart, they branch off and become a network of smaller and smaller arteries finally ending in the smallest of all vessels, the capillaries.

The circulatory system transports nutrients and oxygen to every part of the body. It also picks up wastes and carries them to the lungs, the liver, and the kidneys so the body can expel them. There are very few parts of the body that can survive without the circulatory system. The only places that don't have blood vessels are the fingernails and toenails, tooth enamel, the cornea of the eyes, and the dead outer layers of skin and hair.

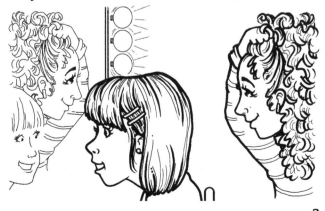

6

3

FROM HEAD TO TOE

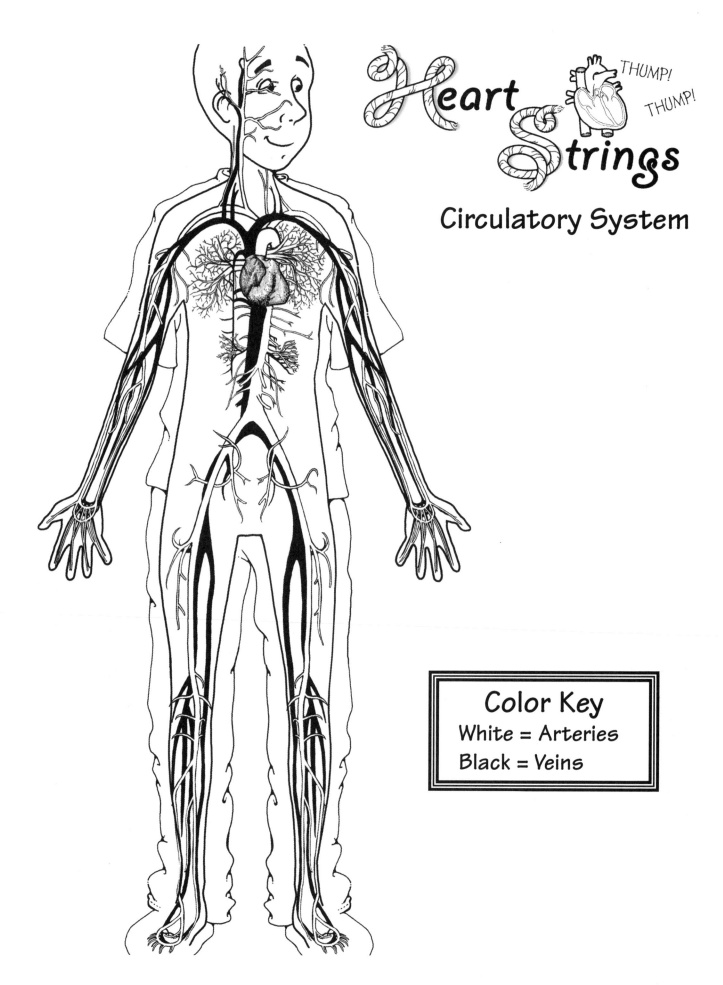

Heart Strings

THUMP! THUMP!

Circulatory System

Color Key
White = Arteries
Black = Veins

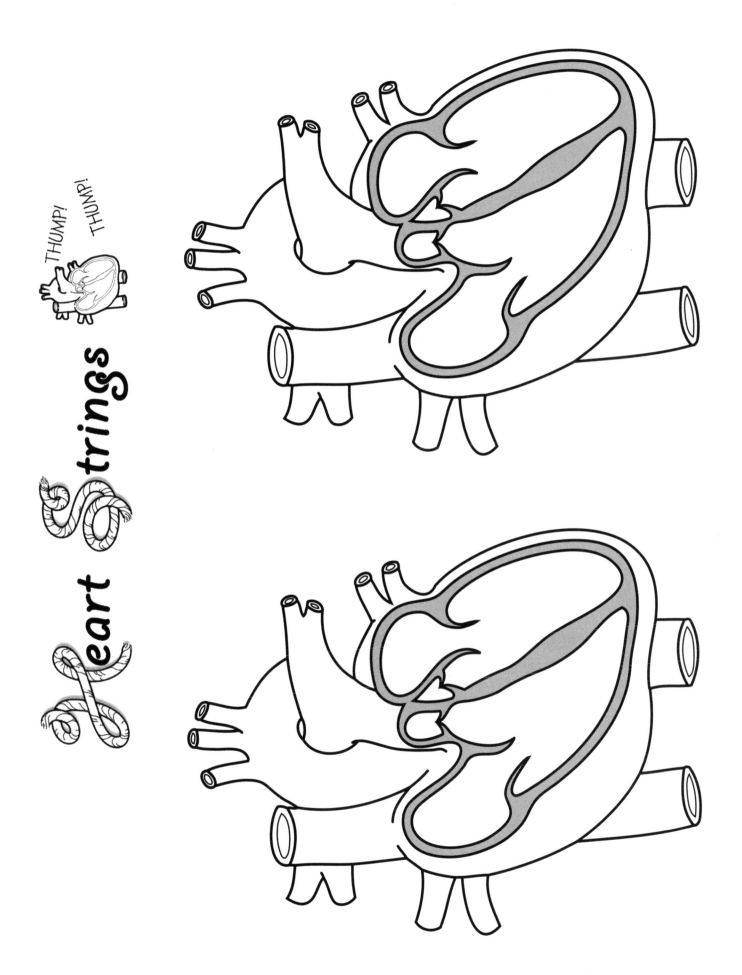

Heart Strings

THUMP! THUMP!

Heart Strings

THUMP!
THUMP!

Connecting Learning

CONNECTING LEARNING

1. What are the components of the circulatory system?

2. Compare and contrast the arteries, veins, and capillaries.

3. Why is the circulatory system important to us?

4. How do our lungs work with our circulatory system?

5. Why do you think our capillaries are so thin?

Connecting Learning

6. Has a doctor ever had to take blood from you to see why you were sick? If so, how did he or she take it?

7. What did you learn from this experience?

8. What are you wondering now?

YA GOTTA HAVE HEART!

Topic
Human heart

Key Questions
1. How much force is needed to pump the blood out of your heart?
2. How much blood does your heart pump in one beat?

Learning Goals
Students will:
- use a tennis ball to experience the force needed to pump blood, and
- determine the amount of blood per stroke their hearts pump.

Guiding Documents
Project 2061 Benchmark
- *Use numerical data in describing and comparing objects and events.*

NRC Standards
- *Use mathematics in all aspects of scientific inquiry.*
- *Mathematics is important in all aspects of scientific inquiry.*

NCTM Standards 2000*
- *Understand various meanings of multiplication and division*
- *Understand the effects of multiplying and dividing whole numbers*
- *Recognize and apply mathematics in contexts outside of mathematics*

Math
Number and operations
   multiplication
   division

Science
Life science
   human body
     heart

Integrated Processes
Observing
Comparing and contrasting
Interpreting data
Applying

Materials
Tennis balls
Calculators
Tape measures (see *Management 3*)
Straight edges
Student page

Background Information
The heart contains two coordinated pumps and is divided into four chambers. Four one-way valves allow blood to flow through the four chambers in only one direction. The heart is a powerful muscle that continuously pumps oxygen and nutrients around the body. When the body is at rest, it takes approximately one minute for blood to make the full circuit through the lungs and body.

In this experience, students will "feel" the force required by the heart to pump the blood when they repeatedly squeeze a tennis ball. After squeezing it 60 times in a minute, they will gain an appreciation for the hard work this muscle does.

Stroke volume is the amount of blood pumped by the heart in one beat. Its precise calculation requires invasive tests, but students can make rough estimates using a few simple formulas and average values. Stroke volume is equal to cardiac output divided by normal pulse rate. Cardiac output is the amount of blood pumped by the heart in one minute. It can be calculated using the body's surface area and the cardiac index. The average cardiac index of 2.75 liters/m^2/minute is used in this activity, which should be fairly accurate for most upper elementary and middle school students. Students will be amazed when they discover how many liters of blood their heart pumps in a day.

Management
1. It's ideal if each student has a tennis ball to squeeze. If you have trouble finding enough tennis balls from students in the class, ask a local tennis club or high school tennis coach to give you some old balls.
2. If you want the lesson to be more visual, have students bring in empty one- or two-liter bottles to represent the average amount of blood pumped by the hearts of your students in an hour (a day is too much!).
3. If students do not know their heights in centimeters, they will need to use metric tape measures to find out. These are available from AIMS (item number 1926).

Procedure

Part One

1. Ask the first *Key Question* and state the first *Learning Goal.*
2. Distribute the student page and tennis balls. Have the students squeeze the balls 60 times in one minute.
3. Discuss their impressions of how the hard the heart works.

Part Two

1. Ask the second *Key Question* and state the second *Learning Goal.*
2. Tell the students that they are going to do some calculations to find out how much blood their hearts pump with each beat.
3. Ask students to look over the information they will need for calculating their stroke volume—the amount of blood pumped in one beat of their heart.
4. If any student doesn't know how tall he or she is in centimeters, give them the opportunity to find out. Have them use their heights and weights to determine their body surface areas.
5. Distribute calculators and have students use the formula to determine their cardiac outputs in liters per minute.
6. Show students how to take their pulse by gently placing their first two fingers on one hand alongside their larynx. For most people, it's easiest to find it on the right side of their larynx. Give students time to locate their pulses.
7. Discuss how they will count their pulse for only 10 seconds because it sometimes is difficult to keep track of it for a minute. Ask students what they will need to do to find their pulse rate for a minute if they only count it for 10 seconds. [Multiply by six because there are 60 seconds in a minute (10 x 6 = 60)]
8. Invite the students to get ready to count their pulse rates. Tell them when to begin and when to stop. Have them jot this number down on the backs of their papers and multiply by six. Tell them that they will take it again to see how close their results are. Do it a third time, and encourage students to find the mean or to cross out the high and low readings and use the median. Have them record this value and divide their cardiac output by their normal pulse rate to find their stroke volume.
9. Discuss with the student how to find how many liters of blood their heart pumps in one minute, one hour, and one day. Have them perform their individual calculations and compare.
10. If desired, have students fill two-liter bottles to represent the amount of blood pumped by their hearts in one hour.

Connecting Learning

1. Were you surprised at the force it takes for the heart to pump blood? Explain.
2. Describe how you felt after one minute of squeezing the ball.
3. Why do you think you were supposed to squeeze the ball 60 times in a minute? [This is about what a normal pulse rate is for an adult.]
4. Could you physically keep up the squeezing of the ball all day long? Explain.
5. What new appreciation do you have for your heart?
6. What does stroke volume mean? [The amount of blood pumped in one beat of the heart.]
7. How much blood does your heart pump in one day? Does this mean that your body contains that much blood? Explain.
8. Why were our amounts different?
9. Do you think this amount will stay the same all your life? Explain.
10. What are you wondering now?

♥ YA GOTTA HAVE HEART!

Key Questions

1. How much force is needed to pump the blood out of your heart?

2. How much blood does your heart pump in one beat?

Learning Goals

Students will:

- use a tennis ball to experience the force needed to pump blood, and

- determine the amount of blood per stroke their hearts pump.

YA GOTTA HAVE HEART!

Try to do the heart's work:

The heart is a powerful muscle. To get a grasp on how hard it works for you, try this. Take a tennis ball in your hand. The force needed to squeeze the tennis ball is similar to the force needed to squeeze the blood out of your heart. Squeeze the ball 10 times. Now, squeeze it 60 times in one minute. You now have an idea of how hard your heart works!

Calculate your heart's stroke volume:

The stroke volume is how much blood your heart pumps in one heartbeat. You need tests with special machines to accurately measure stroke volume, but you can make a rough estimate by doing a few calculations. These are the formulas you will be using:

Cardiac output = Cardiac index x Body surface area

Stroke volume = Cardiac output ÷ Normal pulse rate

To calculate your body surface area, use the chart at the right. Place a straight edge to connect your height in centimeters and your weight in pounds. The place where the straightedge crosses the center line is your body surface area. Record it below. We will be using 2.75 liters/m²/minute as the cardiac index. This is an average for children from ages 10 to 13. Complete the calculations to find your cardiac output.

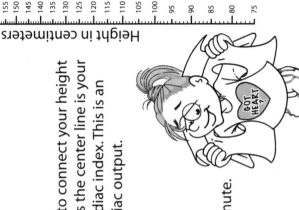

Weight in pounds

300 290 280 270 260 250 240 230 220 210 200 190 180 170 160 150 140 130 120 110 100 90 80 70 60 50 40 35

Body surface area in square meters

3.00 2.90 2.80 2.70 2.60 2.50 2.40 2.30 2.20 2.10 2.00 1.95 1.90 1.85 1.80 1.75 1.70 1.65 1.60 1.55 1.50 1.45 1.40 1.35 1.30 1.25 1.20 1.15 1.10 1.05 1.00 .95 .90 .85 .80 .75 .70 .65 .60 .55 .50

Height in centimeters

220 215 210 205 200 195 190 185 180 175 170 165 160 155 150 145 140 135 130 125 120 115 110 105 100 95 90 85 80 75

Body surface area	x	Cardiac index	=	Cardiac output
m²	x	2.75 L/m²/minute	=	L/minute

Take your resting pulse for 10 seconds and record your normal pulse rate for one minute. Complete the calculations to find your stroke volume.

Cardiac output	÷	Normal pulse rate	=	Stroke volume
L/minute	÷	beats/minute	=	L

When at rest, how many liters of blood does your heart pump in:
One minute?   One hour?   One day?

Connecting Learning

1. Were you surprised at the force it takes for the heart to pump blood? Explain.

2. Describe how you felt after one minute of squeezing the ball.

3. Why do you think you were supposed to squeeze the ball 60 times in a minute?

4. Could you physically keep up the squeezing of the ball all day long? Explain.

5. What new appreciation do you have for your heart?

Ya Gotta Have Heart!

Connecting Learning

6. What does stroke volume mean?

7. How much blood does your heart pump in one day? Does this mean that your body contains that much blood? Explain.

8. Why were our amounts different?

9. Do you think this amount will stay the same all your life? Explain.

10. What are you wondering now?

How Does Your Heart Rate?

Topic
Heart rate

Key Questions
1. What is your pulse rate?
2. How is your pulse rate affected by exercise?

Learning Goals
Students will:
- measure their resting pulse rates,
- investigate how their pulse rates change with exercise, and
- relate the increase in their pulse rates to the amount of blood their hearts are pumping.

Guiding Documents
Project 2061 Benchmarks
- *Use numerical data in describing and comparing objects and events.*
- *Mathematical ideas can be represented concretely, graphically, and symbolically.*
- *Tables and graphs can show how values of one quantity are related to values of another.*

NRC Standards
- *Use mathematics in all aspects of scientific inquiry.*
- *Mathematics is important in all aspects of scientific inquiry.*

NCTM Standards 2000*
- *Collect data using observations, surveys, and experiments*
- *Represent data using tables and graphs such as line plots, bar graphs, and line graphs*

Math
Graphing
    bar graph
Number and operations
    multiplication
Measurement
    time

Science
Life science
    human body
        heart rate

Integrated Processes
Observing
Comparing and contrasting
Collecting and recording data
Interpreting data
Generalizing

Materials
Stopwatch or clock with second hand
Student pages
Calculators, optional

Background Information
Pulse rate is the number of heart beats in one minute. When the heart contracts to push blood out into the rest of the body, it causes a wave of pressure. It is that wave that creates the pulse.

There are many things that can alter one's pulse rate.
- Strenuous activity will increase it because the body needs more oxygen. The blood carries oxygen throughout the body and carries carbon dioxide back to the lungs to be exhaled.
- Being frightened, excited, or nervous causes our bodies to produce more adrenaline. Adrenaline is a signal for the heart to pump faster.
- After a meal, our heart rate is higher because the heart is sending a greater blood flow to the digestive system.
- When we are feverish, our hearts tend to pump faster because the blood carries the heat to the body's surface and helps to cool it. The heart must work very hard to maintain our 98.6°F temperature.

Students will determine their resting pulse rates and then their pulse rates for various activities. The resting pulse rates of elementary students will vary greatly, often between 60 and 110. Adults generally have a slower resting pulse rate, averaging 70 or less. It is important that the students' pulse rates return to normal before performing an exercise. The amount of time it takes after exercise for the pulse to return to normal is the recovery time. Generally speaking, the shorter the recovery time, the higher the fitness level.

Management

1. Have students work in groups of four.
2. Be sensitive to students who may have disabilities or are not able to perform some of the exercises.

Procedure

1. Ask the *Key Questions* and state the *Learning Goals*.
2. Divide student into groups and distribute a stopwatch to each group and the student pages to each student.
3. Go over the roles that students will be filling as they complete the activity. Demonstrate the proper procedure for each of the exercises, emphasizing the importance of safety, especially during the chair step.
4. Review the procedure for finding pulse by placing two fingers (not the thumb) on the side of the neck. Although there are many places on the body at which the pulse can be felt (the underside of the wrist, behind the knee, back behind the ankle on the inside of the leg), it is easiest for students to consistently locate it on the side of the larynx.
5. Have students sit quietly for a minute and then take their pulse rates for 10 seconds and record it on their student pages. Review the reason for taking the pulse rate for 10 seconds and then multiplying by six. [It's much easier to count accurately over a short period of time like 10 seconds than to try and count for an entire minute.]
6. Allow time for students to find and record their pulse rates for all the activities, letting the pulse rate return to normal between exercises. (Sudents can take on the role of timer or recorder while they wait for their heart rates to return to normal.)
7. Direct them to graph the results of their group members.
8. Discuss what they observe and the conclusions they can make.

Connecting Learning

1. How did your resting pulse rate compare to that of others in your group?
2. What was the range of resting pulse rates in your group?
3. How was your pulse rate affected by exercise?
4. How did this compare to the others in your group?
5. Which activity caused your pulse rate to increase the most?
6. Was this true for all members of your group? What might be reasons for any differences?
7. How did the change in pulse rates show in your graph?
8. Why do you think your heart beat faster?
9. What are you wondering now?

*   Reprinted with permission from *Principles and Standards for School Mathematics,* 2000 by the National Council of Teachers of Mathematics. All rights reserved.

How Does Your Heart Rate?

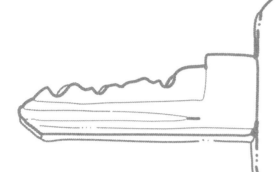

Key Questions

1. What is your pulse rate?

2. How is your pulse rate affected by exercise?

Learning Goals

Students will:

- measure their resting pulse rates,

- investigate how their pulse rates change with exercise, and

- relate the increase in their pulse rates to the amount of blood their hearts are pumping.

How Does Your Heart Rate?

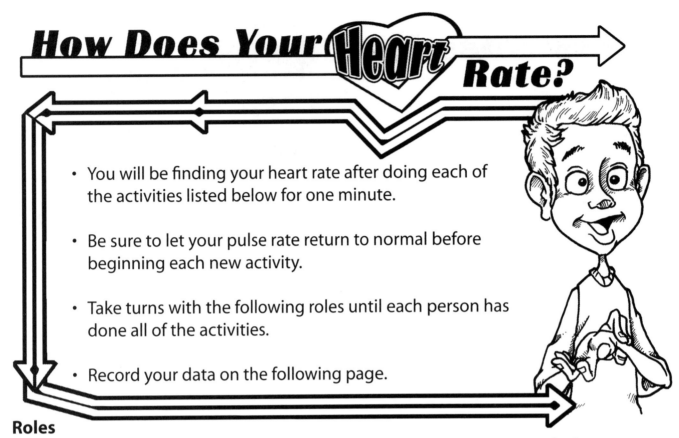

- You will be finding your heart rate after doing each of the activities listed below for one minute.

- Be sure to let your pulse rate return to normal before beginning each new activity.

- Take turns with the following roles until each person has done all of the activities.

- Record your data on the following page.

Roles

Timer: Tell the group members when to start and stop their exercises and when to start and stop finding their pulse rates. They should do each activity for exactly one minute. They should find their pulse rates immediately after completing each exercise.

Recorder: Record each person's pulse rate for 10 seconds in the appropriate spot on that person's student page.

Exercisers: Do each of the activities for exactly one minute. As soon as you stop, count the number of times your heart beats in 10 seconds.

Activities

Walking in place: Stand in one place and move your legs as though you are walking.

Jumping jacks: Jump in the air, bringing your hands together above your head as you spread your legs wide. Jump again, bringing your arms to your sides and your legs together. Repeat.

Chair steps: With a partner holding the back of a chair, step onto the seat with one foot. Bring the other foot up to the chair seat and put the first foot back on the floor. Bring the second foot back to the floor. Repeat.

How Does Your Heart Rate?

Record your data in the table.

Heart rate for 10 seconds	x 6 =	Heart rate per minute
Sitting	x 6 =	
Walking in place	x 6 =	
Jumping jacks	x 6 =	
Chair step	x 6 =	

Graph the results from your group.

Group Members:

A. _____

C. _____

B. _____

D. _____

Heart Rate (per minute)

260
240
220
200
180
160
140
120
100
80
60
40
20

A B C D	A B C D	A B C D	A B C D
Sitting	Walking in Place	Jumping Jacks	Chair Step

Activity

What conclusions can you draw from the data?

Connecting Learning

1. How did your resting pulse rate compare to that of others in your group?

2. What was the range of resting pulse rates in your group?

3. How was your pulse rate affected by exercise?

4. How did this compare to the others in your group?

5. Which activity caused your pulse rate to increase the most?

Connecting Learning

6. Was this true for all members of your group? What might be reasons for any differences?

7. How did the change in pulse rates show in your graph?

8. Why do you think your heart beat faster?

9. What are you wondering now?

Isn't It Interesting...
Heart Smart

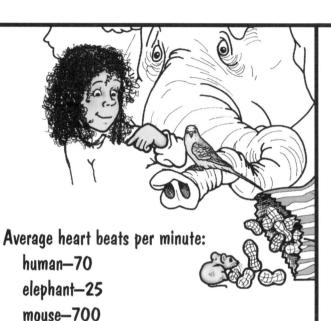

Average heart beats per minute:
- human—70
- elephant—25
- mouse—700
- parakeet—1000

Your heart is about the size of your fist. It weighs less than 455 grams (1 pound).

For a 70-year-old person, his or her will have beat about 2500 million times and pumped about 227 million liters (60 million gallons) of blood!

Your heart is made of a one-of-a-kind muscle; it contracts and relaxes in a rhythm. It's this rhythmic action that pumps blood throughout your body.

Breathe In, Breathe Out

Topic
Respiratory system

Key Question
How can a model of the respiratory system demonstrate the mechanical action of the lungs?

Learning Goals
Students will:
- learn the major parts of the respiratory system,
- construct a working model of the respiratory system, and
- identify and describe the functions of the parts of the respiratory system.

Guiding Documents
Project 2061 Benchmarks
- *Like other animals, human beings have body systems for obtaining and providing energy, defense, reproduction, and the coordination of body functions.*
- *To burn food for the release of energy stored in it, oxygen must be supplied to cells, and carbon dioxide removed. Lungs take in oxygen for the combustion of food and they eliminate the carbon dioxide produced. The urinary system disposes of dissolved waste molecules, the intestinal tract removes solid wastes, and the skin and lungs rid the body of heat energy. The circulatory system moves all these substances to or from cells where they are needed or produced, responding to changing demands.*
- *Models are often used to think about processes that happen too slowly, too quickly, or on too small a scale to observe directly, or that are too vast to be changed deliberately, or that are potentially dangerous.*

NRC Standard
- *The human organism has systems for digestion, respiration, reproduction, circulation, excretion, movement, control, and coordination, and for protection from disease. These systems interact with one another.*

Science
Life science
  human body
    respiratory system

Integrated Processes
Observing
Comparing and contrasting
Modeling
Applying

Materials
For each group:
  two-liter plastic bottle
  two flexible plastic drinking straws
  modeling clay
  two small round balloons
  transparent tape
  Lung Model Background page

For each student:
  The Respiratory System rubber band book
  student page

Background Information
In the human body, the oxygen in the air is transferred through the lungs to the blood that then carries the oxygen throughout the body. Carbon dioxide, a waste product, is picked up by the blood, carried back to the lungs, and expelled to the air.

Breathing starts with a muscle at the bottom of the lungs called the *diaphragm*. The diaphragm pulls downward, pulling air through the *nasal cavity*, down the *trachea*, through the *bronchi*, and into the lungs. The bronchi branch into *bronchioles* that end in air sacs called *alveoli*. It is at the alveoli that the blood's oxygen/carbon dioxide exchange occurs. All of these parts work together to form the respiratory system.

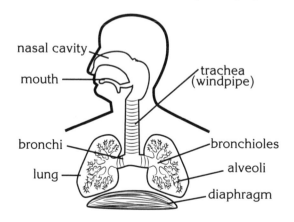

In this activity, students construct a model of the respiratory system that models the mechanical action of filling and emptying the lungs.

Key Vocabulary

Alveoli: tiny, thin-walled sacs in the lungs where the exchange of oxygen and carbon dioxide takes place

Bronchi: two air tubes that branch off the trachea and carry air directly into the lungs

Bronchioles: smaller tubes connected to the bronchi and ending in alveoli

Trachea: windpipe connecting the throat to the lungs

Diaphragm: the muscle that causes the lungs to inflate and deflate

Lungs: respiratory organs in the chest that bring oxygen into the body and expel carbon dioxide from the body

Management

1. Clean each two-liter plastic bottle with warm water and soap and remove the label. If necessary, use a commercial goo remover or citrus juice to clean the excess glue.
2. For this activity, use small balloons of the type commonly sold as water balloons or the next larger size.
3. Schedule time to build the model yourself. Doing so will help you better guide your students.

Procedure

1. Distribute *The Respiratory System* rubber band book to each student. Show them how to fold it in half and then in half again so that the pages are in order.
2. Have students read through the book, then discuss what they learned and clarify any questions they may have about the functions of the various parts of the respiratory system.
3. Have students get into groups of two or three and distribute the materials and the *Model Construction* page to each group.
4. Allow time for groups to follow the instructions and complete their models, providing assistance as needed.
5. When groups have completed their models, distribute the student page to every student.
6. Instruct the students to gently squeeze the sides of the bottle and to observe the action of the balloons.
7. Have the students sketch the shape of the balloons before and after taking a breath (squeezing the bottle).
8. As students take turns operating the model, tell them to think about how the model is like a real set of lungs and how the model is different from real lungs. Have them record their thoughts on the student page.
9. Distribute a copy of the *Lung Model Background* page to each group and tell them to label the parts of the respiratory system and tape the pattern to the back of the bottle.

Connecting Learning

1. What part of the model represents the trachea? [the straight sections of the plastic straws]
2. What represents the bronchia on your model? [the bent sections]
3. The lungs are what part of your model? [balloons]
4. What part of the model acts like the diaphragm? [the plastic sides of the bottle]
5. Why do the balloons inflate when you squeeze and hold the sides of the bottle? [decreases volume of air in bottle, which increases the air pressure]
6. What happens if you block the top of the straws (trachea) with your finger? [balloons cannot inflate or deflate]
7. Use your model to describe choking.
8. How is your model is like a real pair of lungs? How is it different?
9. What are you wondering now?

Internet Connections

KidsHealth®
http://kidshealth.org/kid/htbw/
Select the lungs from the scrolling list for information on the lungs and respiratory system, diagrams, movies, and more.

Solutions

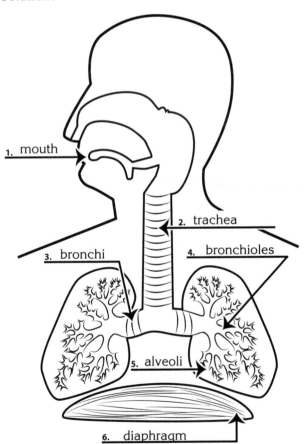

1. mouth
2. trachea
3. bronchi
4. bronchioles
5. alveoli
6. diaphragm

Breathe In, Breathe Out

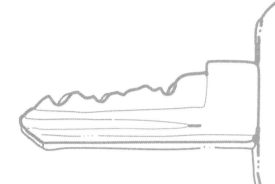

Key Question

How can a model of the respiratory system demonstrate the mechanical action of the lungs?

Learning Goals

- learn the major parts of the respiratory system,

- construct a working model of the respiratorysystem, and

- identify and describe the functions of the parts of the respiratory system.

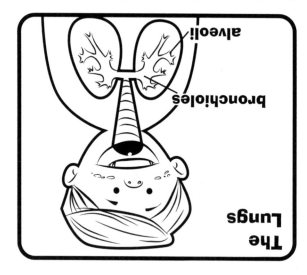

Your lungs are the organs that get oxygen into your blood. They also remove carbon dioxide from your body. Inside your lungs are bronchioles. They are smaller tubes that connect to the bronchi. These bronchioles end in alveoli. Alveoli are tiny, thin-walled sacs where the exchange of oxygen and carbon dioxide takes place.

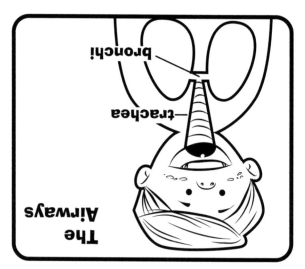

Air enters your body through your mouth and/or nose. It goes from there down the trachea. This is your "windpipe." It's a tube that connects your throat to your lungs. At the end of the trachea are the bronchi. They are tubes that branch off into each lung.

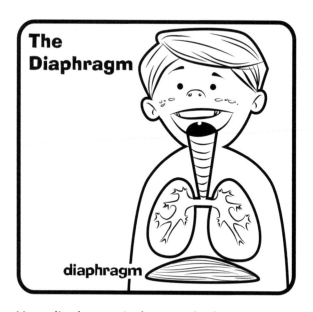

Your diaphragm is the muscle that causes your lungs to inflate and deflate. The diaphragm contracts, pulling air into the lungs. When it relaxes, air is pushed out of the lungs.

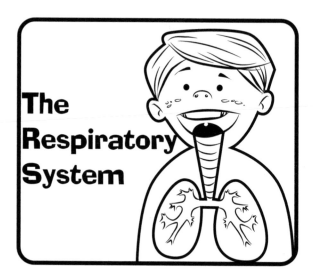

Your body needs oxygen to survive. Your respiratory system is responsible for taking oxygen from the air and getting it into your body. We call this process breathing, or respiration. The respiratory system is made up of several parts.

Breathe In, Breathe Out

Model Construction

Materials

Two flexible drinking straws

Tape

Clay

Two balloons

Two-liter bottle

Lung Model Background page

Directions

1. Stretch out the flexible part of each straw. Bend each straw into the shape of a hockey stick.

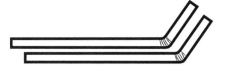

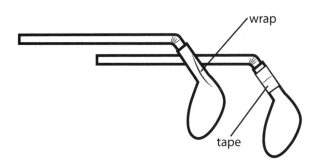

2. Stretch the balloons two or three times without inflating them. Tightly wrap the neck of a balloon around the short end of the straw and then tape around the neck to hold the balloon in place.

3. Place the two straws side by side to form a "Y". Put tape around both straws along the longer sections of the straws.

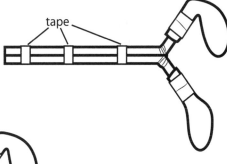

4. Wrap the clay ball around the ends of the straws.

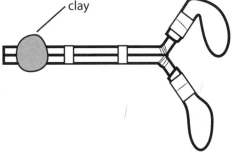

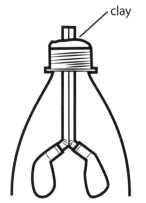

5. Hold the balloon ends together, insert the balloon ends into the neck of the bottle, and lower the straws until the clay ball is resting on the mouth of the bottle. Carefully push the clay around the ends of the straws to make an airtight seal.

Breathe In, Breathe Out

1. Draw the shape of the lungs (balloons) before taking a breath.

2. Draw the shape of the lungs (balloons) after taking a breath.

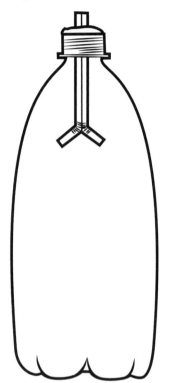

3. Describe how your model is like a real pair of lungs.

4. Describe how your model is different from a real pair of lungs.

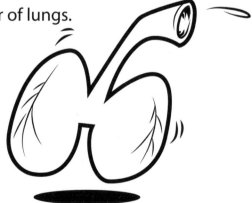

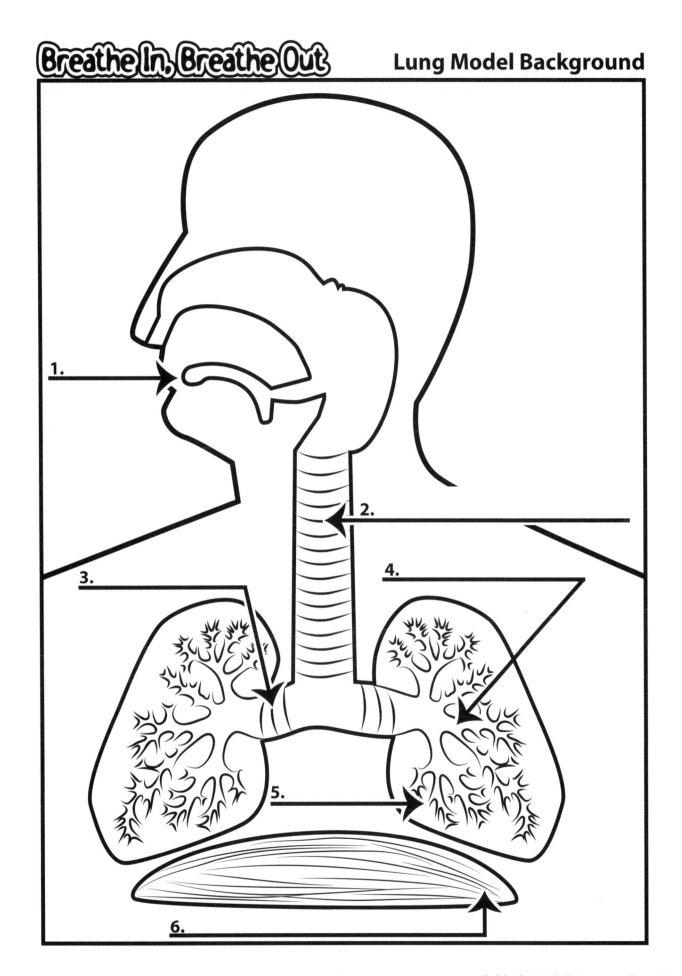

1. _____

2. _____

3. _____

4. _____

5. _____

6. _____

71

Breathe In, Breathe Out

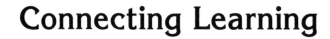

Connecting Learning

1. What part of the model represents the trachea?

2. What represents the bronchia on your model?

3. The lungs are what part of your model?

4. What part of the model acts like the diaphragm?

5. Why do the balloons inflate when you squeeze and hold the sides of the bottle?

Breathe In, Breathe Out

Connecting Learning

6. What happens if you block the top of the straws (trachea) with your finger?

7. Use your model to describe choking.

8. How is your model is like a real pair of lungs? How is it different?

9. What are you wondering now?

Take a Breather

Topic
Lung capacity

Key Questions
1. What is your vital capacity?
2. Do our class data show any relationship between lung capacity and gender, height, or amount of exercise?

Learning Goals
Students will:
- measure their expiratory reserve volume and vital capacity;
- organize and display the data in a manner of their choosing; and
- determine if the class data show any relationship between lung capacity and gender, height, or amount of exercise.

Guiding Documents
Project 2061 Benchmarks
- *Like other animals, human beings have body systems for obtaining and providing energy, defense, reproduction, and the coordination of body functions.*
- *Graphs can show a variety of possible relationships between two variables. As one variable increases uniformly, the other may do one of the following: always keep the same proportion to the first, increase or decrease steadily, increase or decrease faster and faster, get closer and closer to some limiting value, reach some intermediate maximum or minimum, alternately increase and decrease indefinitely, increase and decrease in steps, or do something different from any of these.*
- *Find the mean and median of a set of data.*
- *Organize information in simple tables and graphs and identify relationships they reveal.*
- *Read simple tables and graphs produced by others and describe in words what they show.*

NRC Standards
- *Use appropriate tools and techniques to gather, analyze, and interpret data.*
- *Use mathematics in all aspects of scientific inquiry.*
- *The human organism has systems for digestion, respiration, reproduction, circulation, excretion, movement, control, and coordination, and for protection from disease. These systems interact with one another.*

NCTM Standards 2000*
- *Select and apply techniques and tools to accurately find length, area, volume, and angle measures to appropriate levels of precision*
- *Formulate questions, design studies, and collect data about a characteristic shared by two populations or different characteristics within one population*
- *Select, create, and use appropriate graphical representations of data, including histograms, box plots, and scatterplots*
- *Find, use, and interpret measures of center and spread, including mean and interquartile range*

Math
Data analysis
    average
    graphing
Measurement
    length
    unit conversions

Science
Life science
    human body
        lung capacity

Integrated Processes
Observing
Collecting and recording data
Organizing data
Interpreting data
Drawing conclusions

Materials
Take a Breather rubber band book
#19 rubber bands
Nine-inch balloons
Metric tape measures
Class data table (see *Management 2*)
Chart paper (see *Management 3*)
Markers (see *Management 3*)
Student page

Key Vocabulary
Expiratory reserve volume: amount of breath that can be forced out of lungs after normal exhalation
Tidal volume: amount of air breathed in or out of the lungs during normal breathing
Vital capacity: amount of air that can be breathed out after taking as large a breath as possible

Background Information

Lung capacity is the total volume of air that the lungs can hold. This volume can be determined by measurements and calculations and varies from person to person. Several factors influence total lung capacity, including gender, height, and activity level. Generally speaking, females, shorter people, smokers, non-athletes, and those living at low altitudes will have smaller lung capacities than males, taller people, non-smokers, athletes, and those living at high altitudes.

Two of the values associated with lung capacity will be measured by students during this activity: expiratory reserve volume and vital capacity. Expiratory reserve volume is the amount of breath that can be forced out of the lungs after normal exhalation. Vital capacity is the amount of air that can be breathed out after taking as large a breath as possible. The expiratory reserve volume will be small compared to vital capacity, but it makes an important point that most students don't realize—there is still air left in our lungs after we exhale during normal respiration.

Students will measure these two values by exhaling air into a balloon and measuring its circumference. While the circumference measurement does not actually measure the volume, it does give a value that can be used to make relative comparisons. Because circumference is a linear measurement and volume is a cubic measurement, what may seem like a small difference in circumference translates into a more significant difference in volume. For example, an increase in circumference from 54 to 55 centimeters represents 1 cm, or less than a 2% increase. By contrast, the difference in volume (assuming the balloon is roughly spherical) is about 48 cm^3, or more than a 5% increase.

Management

1. This activity is divided into two parts—data collection and data analysis. If desired, the parts can be done on separate days.
2. The class data table provided can be displayed using a projection device or re-created on the board or chart paper. The data need to be recorded in such a way that all students will be able to see and read them. You can also enter the data into a spreadsheet program on the computer.
3. Each pair of students will need a piece of chart paper and markers in order to generate a data display. Alternatively, enter the class data in the computer and have students use a spreadsheet program (such as Excel) or the website listed in *Internet Connections* to generate their data displays.

4. Set up height measurement stations by taping metric tape measure to the wall end-to-end with the zero ends touching the floor. Students can come to these stations, remove their shoes, and have their heights measured.

5. Metric tape measures are available from AIMS (item number 1926).

Procedure

Part One: Data Collection

1. Distribute the *Take a Breather* rubber band book. Have students read through it, following the instructions as they go along.
2. Discuss the terms that the book introduced. Explain that students will be doing an experiment to determine their expiratory reserve volume and their vital capacity.
3. Distribute a copy of the student page to each student. Invite a student to the front of the room and explain that you will go through the steps in the procedure with this student so that everyone can see what to do.
4. Begin by having the student go to one of the height measuring stations and remove his or her shoes. Show the class how to properly measure height by having the student stand straight with his or her back against the wall. Place a file folder or similar thin, rigid object on the top of the student's head and hold it perpendicular to the wall so that it touches the tape measure. Round to the nearest half-centimeter and tell students the number. Ask them what this student's height is in centimeters. (They should realize that they will need to add 100 to this number for the total height in centimeters, since there are two tape measures on the wall.)

5. Follow the instructions on the student page and have the student subject complete both tests. (For the demonstration, it is not necessary to do all three trials on both tests.)

6. Pair students and distribute the balloons and tape measures. Allow time for students to collect the data, trading off who is the subject.

Part Two: Data Analysis

1. When all pairs are finished, display the class data table. Point out that the table asks for minutes of exercise per day, not per week. Ask students how they will convert the values they have into the appropriate units. [Divide number of minutes per week by seven.]

2. Allow time for students to make the necessary conversions and then have them share their data. Record it in the data table for the class to see.

3. Discuss the factors that influence lung capacity and ask how the data in this table might be displayed to see if they reflect the differences that "should" exist. [The data could be re-ordered by different characteristics, it could be graphed, it could be displayed on a line plot, etc.]

4. Divide the pairs of students into three groups. Assign each of the groups one of the three characteristics—gender, height, or exercise. Have each of the pairs within the groups come up with a way to display the class data for that characteristic. Give pairs of students a piece of chart paper and markers on which to create their data displays and record their conclusions (or have them use software to generate their data displays).

5. Conduct a time of class sharing where each pair of students shares its data display and conclusions. Compare displays from pair to pair within the same group and from group to group.

6. Discuss whether the class data support the claim that gender, height, and amount of exercise affect lung capacity. If not, discuss possible reasons for the differences.

Connecting Learning

Part One

1. What factors affect a person's lung capacity? [height, gender, exercise habits, etc.]

2. Why do you think athletes sometimes travel to high altitudes to train?

3. What does the expiratory reserve volume show you? [There is still air left in your lungs after you exhale during normal breathing.] Did this surprise you? Why or why not?

4. Is it possible to exhale more air than you inhale? [Yes.] How do you know? [When we were testing our expiratory reserve volume, we exhaled more air after we were "done" exhaling.]

5. Were your results consistent from one trial to the next? If not, what might be some reasons for differences?

6. What was the difference between your expiratory reserve volume average and your vital capacity average? Does this difference reflect the difference in volume? Explain. [No. See *Background Information* for details.]

Part Two

1. How did you and your partner choose to organize your data? Why?

2. How did the way you organized your data compare to others?

3. Did one data display seem more effective than others? Explain.

4. Do our data support the conclusion that males have greater lung capacity than females? Explain.

5. Do our data support the conclusion that more exercise leads to greater lung capacity? Explain.

6. Do our data support the conclusion that taller people have greater lung capacity than shorter people? Explain.

7. Do you think our data would have been different if we had had more variety in the ages, heights, etc., of our subjects?

8. What are you wondering now?

Extensions

1. Challenge students to find their approximate vital capacity as a volume measure (cubic centimeters or milliliters). The formula for volume of a sphere is $4/3\pi r^3$. (Assume that the balloons are spherical.)

2. Have students collect data on their family members and compare those to the class data.

Internet Connections

Learning With NCES Kids' Zone

http://nces.ed.gov/nceskids/createagraph/default.aspx
This website allows you to design, print, and download graphs of any kind using your own data and specifications.

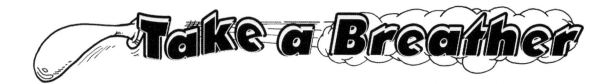

Take a Breather

Key Questions

1. What is your vital capacity?

2. Do our class data show any relationship between lung capacity and gender, height, or amount of exercise?

Learning Goals

- measure their expiratory reserve volume and vital capacity;

- organize and display the data in a manner of their choosing; and

- determine if the class data show any relationship between lung capacity and gender, height, or amount of exercise.

7

There are many factors that can affect your lung capacity. Some of these factors, such as exercise and smoking, can be controlled. Others, such as gender and height, cannot.

Focus on your breathing for a minute. Don't change anything; just pay attention to how you normally breathe. This normal breathing is called *tidal breathing*. The amount of air you are breathing in and out is called the *tidal volume*.

In general, people with the characteristics listed on the left side of the table will have greater lung capacities than those with the characteristics listed on the right side of the table.

Larger Capacity	Smaller Capacity
Males	Females
Taller people	Shorter people
Non-smokers	Smokers
Athletes	Non-athletes
People living at high altitudes	People living at low altitudes

Take a Breather

8

1

Take a deep breath. Inhale as much air as you possibly can. Now, exhale all of the air. Try to empty your lungs completely. The air you just exhaled is your *vital capacity.* It's the volume of air that can be exhaled after filling the lungs as full as possible.

This air is called your *expiratory reserve volume.* It's the amount of air typically left in your lungs during normal (tidal) breathing.

This is not all of the air in your lungs, however. There is some amount of air that always remains in the lungs. It cannot be exhaled. This amount, plus the maximum amount you can inhale equal your total lung capacity.

Now, at the end of a normal breath, instead of inhaling again, try to exhale some more air. Were you able to force more air out of your lungs? If you were breathing normally, you should have been able to expel more air.

Take a Breather

Record the following information about the subject.

Name: _____

Gender: _____

Height: _____

Minutes of strenuous exercise per week: _____

Expiratory Reserve Volume

1. Have the subject fully inflate the balloon several times to stretch it out.
2. Instruct the subject to breathe normally, taking neither deep nor shallow breaths. After exhaling normally, have the subject blow the rest (expiratory reserve) into the balloon and pinch it off.
3. Measure the circumference of the balloon at the widest point.
4. Record the data in the table.
5. Repeat the test two more times and find the average.

Trial One	
Trial Two	
Trial Three	
Total	
Average	

Vital Capacity

1. Instruct the subject to take the deepest breath he or she can and to blow every bit of air into the balloon and pinch it off.
2. Measure the circumference of the balloon at the widest point.
3. Record the data in the table.
4. Repeat the test two more times and find the average.

Trial One	
Trial Two	
Trial Three	
Total	
Average	

Class Data Table

Name	Gender	Height (cm)	Minutes Exercise/Day	Average Vital Capacity

Connecting Learning

Part One

1. What factors affect a person's lung capacity?

2. Why do you think athletes sometimes travel to high altitudes to train?

3. What does the expiratory reserve volume show you? Did this surprise you? Why or why not?

4. Is it possible to exhale more air than you inhale? How do you know?

5. Were your results consistent from one trial to the next? If not, what might be some reasons for differences?

Connecting Learning

6. What was the difference between your expiratory reserve volume average and your vital capacity average? Does this difference reflect the difference in volume? Explain.

Connecting Learning

Part Two

1. How did you and your partner choose to organize your data? Why?

2. How did the way you organized your data compare to others?

3. Did one data display seem more effective than others? Explain.

4. Do our data support the conclusion that males have greater lung capacity than females? Explain.

5. Do our data support the conclusion that more exercise leads to greater lung capacity? Explain.

Connecting Learning

6. Do our data support the conclusion that taller people have greater lung capacity than shorter people? Explain.

7. Do you think our data would have been different if we had had more variety in the ages, heights, etc., of our subjects?

8. What are you wondering now?

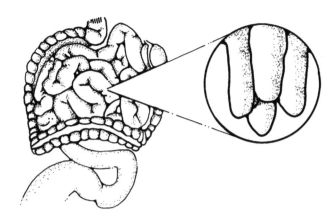

The small intestine has lots of folds and tiny finger-like structures called villi that contain blood vessels. The cells that line these villi absorb the nutrients. The leftovers are passed on to the large intestine.

Digestion is a necessary process that breaks food up into smaller and smaller parts so that the body can absorb the nutrients from the food and give you energy to live.

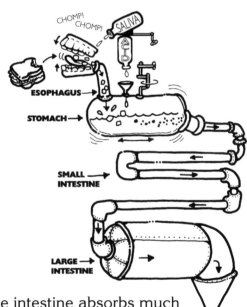

The large intestine absorbs much of the water and you are left with what is politely and correctly called feces. When the time is right, you get rid of the feces and the one-way journey is complete.

Reader's Digestion

Why is **digestion** necessary?
PAGE 2

ONE WAY

PAGE 4 Take a One-Way Journey!

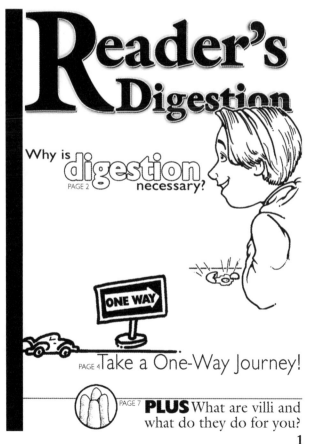

PAGE 7 **PLUS** What are villi and what do they do for you?

Sometimes when you are sick, the food goes the opposite way. If you've ever vomited, you've felt the food go the wrong way on its one-way journey!

There is a strong muscle layer in your esophagus. Because the digestive system is a one-way transportation system for your food, these muscles help to push the food down into your stomach.

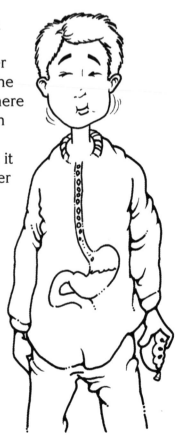

Once the food is in your stomach, its strong muscle layer churns the food. The stomach is also where the food mixes with a very strong acid that helps to break it up into even smaller parts. Your food spends several hours here. It then passes into the small intestine where your body is finally able to absorb it.

Chewing starts the digestive process. Your teeth chop and grind the food. Saliva is added to moisten your food and keep it from sticking to your mouth. Your tongue helps move the food around in your mouth and pushes it to the back of your throat so you can swallow it.

88

Digestion Details

Topic
Digestive system

Key Question
In what organs do the digestive processes occur?

Learning Goals
Students will:
- learn the major digestive organs and their functions, and
- make a simple model of a common digestive process.

Guiding Documents
Project 2061 Benchmarks
- *From food, people obtain energy and materials for body repair and growth. The undigestible parts of food are eliminated.*
- *For the body to use food for energy and building materials, the food must first be digested into molecules that are absorbed and transported to cells.*
- *Like other animals, human beings have body systems for obtaining and providing energy, defense, reproduction, and the coordination of body functions.*

NRC Standard
- *The human organism has systems for digestion, respiration, reproduction, circulation, excretion, movement, control, and coordination, and for protection from disease. These systems interact with one another.*

Science
Life science
   human body
      digestive system

Integrated Processes
Observing
Comparing and contrasting
Modeling
Applying

Materials
For the class:
   oatmeal, 18 oz container
   white vinegar, 16 oz
   baking soda
   Digestive Tract page

For each group:
   four condiment cups, 1 oz
   eyedropper
   coffee stir stick (see *Management 2*)
   paper towels

For each student:
   student pages
   Digestion Details rubber band book
   #19 rubber band

Background Information
The digestive system produces the chemicals used to break down food into nutrients that build and nourish the body's cells, providing the energy needed to sustain life. An overview of the digestive system is illustrated on the *Digestive Tract* page. It describes the passage of food and drink through the body, beginning in the mouth and ending with the release of the body's solid waste.

This activity extends the overview by adding the two sphincter muscles, the common bile duct, the pancreatic duct, and their functions to the digestive description.

Chewed food, moistened by saliva, forms a soft ball called a *bolus*. The bolus passes down the esophagus, through the *lower esophageal sphincter*, into the *stomach*. Acid and other digestive chemicals are added and mixed with the bolus to form a semi-liquid mass of partly digested food called *chyme*. The chyme passes through the *pyloric sphincter* into the first section of the small intestine called the *duodenum*. Digestive chemicals from the liver, gallbladder, and pancreas enter the duodenum through the common bile duct and the pancreatic duct and further digest the chyme. The acidic chyme is neutralized by the addition of the chemical bicarbonate from the pancreas.

Most students have experienced an upset stomach. The nausea they felt may have been followed by the very unpleasant act of vomiting. Vomiting is the body's way of rejecting spoiled food and protecting the body from overeating and overdrinking.

In this activity, saliva, represented by water, adds moisture to oatmeal, forming a bolus. Then the acidic contents of the stomach are modeled by adding vinegar to oatmeal. The bicarbonate produced in the pancreas neutralizes the acidic contents of the stomach. This is modeled when students add baking soda to the bolus of oatmeal and vinegar.

Management

1. Prepare the condiment cups before doing the activity. Each group will need a condiment cup of oatmeal, water, vinegar (half full), and baking soda (half full).
2. Coffee stir sticks can be cut in half. Each group will need half a stick to use for stirring.
3. Eyedroppers (item number 1946) are available from AIMS.
4. Students can work together in groups of three or four.
5. Plan to display the *Digestive Tract* page using a projection device.

Procedure

1. Ask the *Key Question* and state the *Learning Goals*.
2. Display the *Digestive Tract* page and review or introduce the main parts of the human digestive system.
3. Arrange students into working groups. Hand out the rubber band book pages and the #19 rubber bands. Allow time for students to assemble the book and read it. Tell students they will use the information from the book and what they learn from making the model to answer questions on their student pages.
4. Give each group two or three paper towels, an eyedropper, a condiment cup of oatmeal and one of water. Also hand out the student activity pages.
5. Tell students they will use the oatmeal to simulate digestive processes. Direct students to follow the procedures outlined on their student pages.
6. While students are working, distribute the condiment cups of vinegar and baking soda.
7. When students have finished, conclude with a discussion of their answers and the *Connecting Learning* questions.

Connecting Learning

1. What is digestion? [the breaking down of food so it can be used by the body]
2. Why is it necessary that our food be digested? [so it will be small enough to be absorbed by the body and be carried to all our cells]
3. There are two types of digestion: mechanical (which uses a physical force) and chemical (which uses chemicals to break down food). What parts of the body are responsible for mechanical digestion? [teeth as they break the food into smaller bits, tongue as it rolls the food into a ball, stomach as it massages the food]
4. Which parts of the digestive system aid in chemical digestion? [The saliva in our mouths begins to change carbohydrates into simple sugars. The stomach contains acids that break down the food. The liver, gallbladder, and pancreas add chemicals that also break down the food.]
5. Sometimes certain foods can cause upset stomach. People might take an antacid tablet or some baking soda to feel better. What do you think the antacid tablet or baking soda does? [It neutralizes the acid in their stomach.]
6. How do our bodies neutralize the acid in our stomachs? [The pancreas produces chemicals (bicarbonate) that neutralize the acid.]
7. What has to happen to enable food to come up through your esophagus when you vomit? [The lower esophageal sphincter has to open to let food out of the stomach.]
8. How is vomiting different from burping? [Vomiting lets food out of the stomach. Burping lets air out.]
9. What are feces? [solid, indigestible food waste]
10. What do you think would happen if your digestive system quit working altogether? [You would die because your body wouldn't have the food energy required for it to function.]
11. What are you wondering now?

Internet Connections

KidsHealth®
http://kidshealth.org/kid/htbw/
Select the stomach from the scrolling list for information on the stomach and digestive system, diagrams, movies, and more.

DIGESTION DETAILS

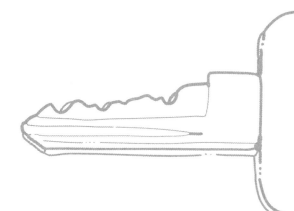

Key Question

In what organs do the digestive processes occur?

Learning Goals

Students will:

- learn the major digestive organs and their functions, and

- make a simple model of a common digestive process.

DiGestion DetaiLs

Digestive Tract

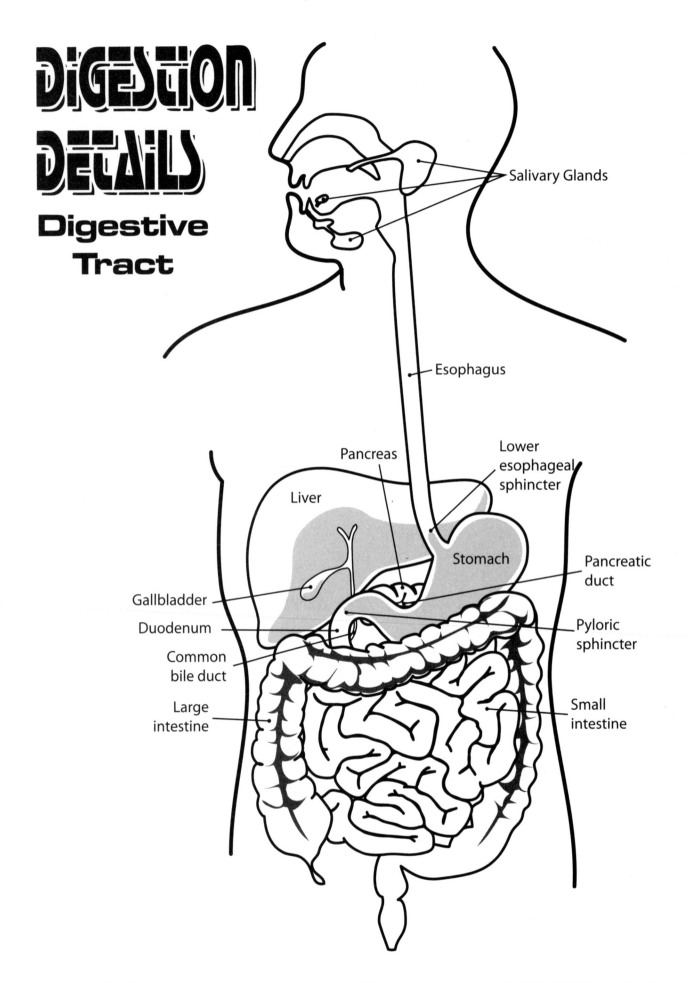

Salivary Glands

Esophagus

Pancreas

Lower esophageal sphincter

Liver

Stomach

Pancreatic duct

Gallbladder

Pyloric sphincter

Duodenum

Common bile duct

Large intestine

Small intestine

92

Now the chyme is ready to be absorbed by tiny blood vessels in the small intestine. The blood carries the nutrients to the cells throughout the body.

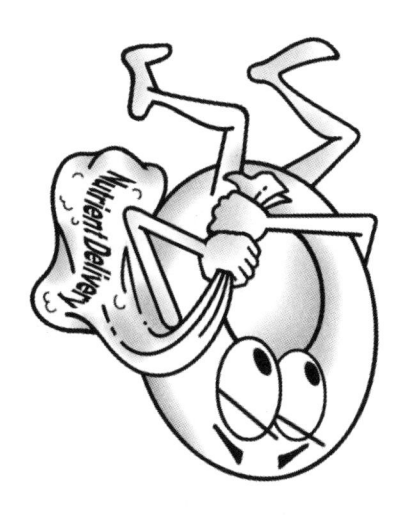

What happens to the food we eat? How does it nourish our bodies? If all our cells need energy to function, where do they get that energy?

Materials that were not digested pass into the large intestine. Here the extra liquid is absorbed. The solid material that remains is called feces. It is excreted through the anus.

Digestion Details

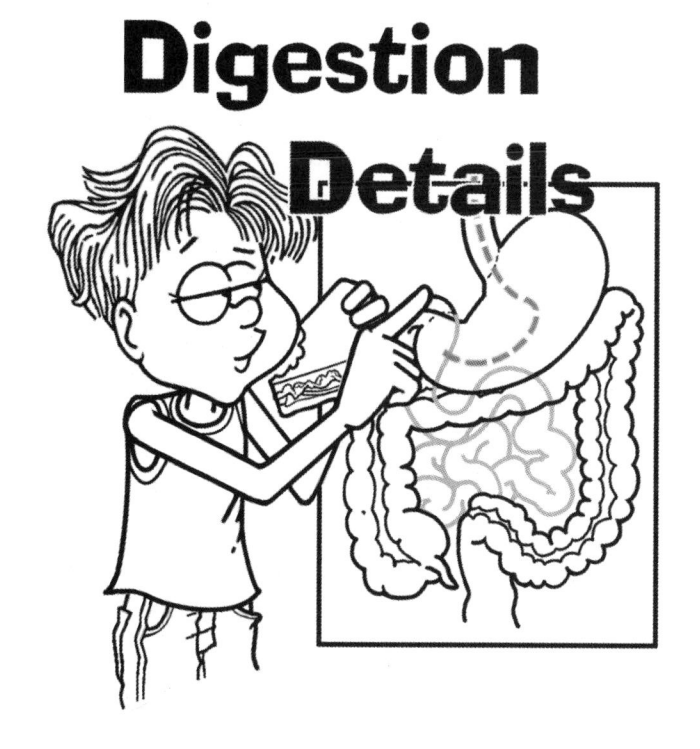

FROM HEAD TO TOE

Another sphincter muscle is at the bottom of the stomach. This is called the pyloric sphincter. When it is closed, the chyme stays in the stomach. When it is open, the chyme passes into the small intestine.

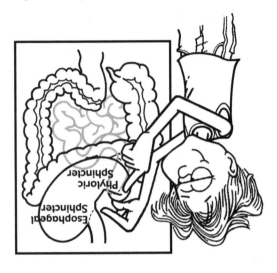

Esophageal Sphincter

Phyloric Sphincter

Digestion starts in the mouth with your teeth and saliva. Your teeth grind the food into smaller bits. Saliva adds moisture to the food. The saliva also begins to break down starches into smaller sugars. The food forms a soft ball called a *bolus*.

In the top portion of the small intestine called the *duodenum*, chemicals from the liver, gallbladder, and pancreas mix with the chyme. These chemicals contain bicarbonates that help to neutralize the chyme.

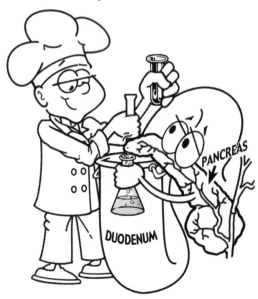

PANCREAS

DUODENUM

Our food gives us the energy to carry out life's functions. How does it go from a big chunk of apple to small enough morsels to feed a tiny, tiny cell? It is through the processes of digestion that food is broken down into forms that our bodies can use.

FROM HEAD TO TOE

© 2010 AIMS Education Foundation

Once the food is passed, the LES closes so that the food stays in the stomach. (Sometimes after eating, the LES will relax and let air from the stomach escape. This results in a burp.)

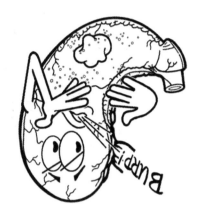

The bolus passes the lower esophageal sphincter (LES). This is a ring-like muscle that opens to let the bolus pass into the stomach.

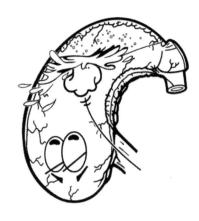

Once the bolus is in the stomach, some wonderful chemical reactions start taking place. Strong acids and other gastric juices are added to the bolus. The stomach muscles massage the bolus and mix these liquids into it. It is now much more soupy than when it was swallowed. This soupy liquid is called chyme.

You swallow the bolus and down it goes through the esophagus. The esophagus is lined with muscles that push the food down. Did you know that you could still swallow food even if you were standing on your head?

FROM HEAD TO TOE

DIGESTION DETAILS

1. Describe and illustrate the dry oatmeal.

2. In what part of the body does the digestive process begin?

3. Use the eyedropper to add drops of water to the oatmeal until it forms a soft ball. This is called a *bolus*. What does the moistened oatmeal represent?

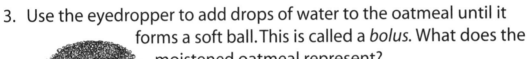

4. What does the oatmeal look like now?

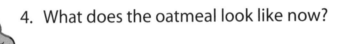

5. What is formed in your mouth to moisten your food as you chew?

6. Name the part of the digestive system that is a hollow tube lined with muscles that push the bolus into the stomach.

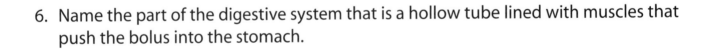

7. What is the function of the lower esophageal sphincter?

DIGESTION DETAILS

8. Explain the digestive process that occurs in the stomach.

9. Add vinegar to the bolus. This mixture is called chyme. What does the vinegar represent?

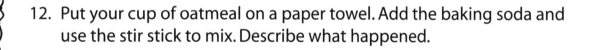

10. How does the chyme enter the small intestine?

11. What is the name of the first part of the small intestine?

12. Put your cup of oatmeal on a paper towel. Add the baking soda and use the stir stick to mix. Describe what happened.

13. How has the oatmeal changed through this process?

14. Why must our food be broken down through the process of digestion?

DIGESTION DETAILS

Connecting Learning

1. What is digestion?

2. Why is it necessary that our food be digested?

3. There are two types of digestion: mechanical (which uses a physical force) and chemical (which uses chemicals to break down food). What parts of the body are responsible for mechanical digestion?

4. Which parts of the digestive system aid in chemical digestion?

5. Sometimes certain foods can cause upset stomach. People might take an antacid tablet or some baking soda to feel better. What do you think the antacid tablet or baking soda does?

DiGESTION DETAILS

Connecting Learning

6. How do our bodies neutralize the acid in our stomachs?

7. What has to happen to enable food to come up through your esophagus when you vomit?

8. How is vomiting different from burping?

9. What are feces?

10. What do you think would happen if your digestive system quit working altogether?

11. What are you wondering now?

The Adventures of PB & J

Topic
Digestive system

Key Question
What happens to a peanut butter and jelly sandwich as it passes through the digestive system?

Learning Goals
Students will:
- learn the major digestive organs and their functions, and
- perform a skit to model how food is processed through the digestive system.

Guiding Documents
Project 2061 Benchmarks
- *From food, people obtain energy and materials for body repair and growth. The undigestible parts of food are eliminated.*
- *For the body to use food for energy and building materials, the food must first be digested into molecules that are absorbed and transported to cells.*
- *Like other animals, human beings have body systems for obtaining and providing energy, defense, reproduction, and the coordination of body functions.*

NRC Standard
- *The human organism has systems for digestion, respiration, reproduction, circulation, excretion, movement, control, and coordination, and for protection from disease. These systems interact with one another.*

Science
Life science
   human body
      digestive system

Integrated Processes
Observing
Comparing and contrasting
Modeling
Generalizing

Materials
For the performance:
   peanut butter and jelly sandwich
   7 quart-size plastic bags, recloseable
   3 marbles
   distilled white vinegar
   baking soda
   3 plastic cups, 9 oz
   condiment cups, 1 oz
   1 plastic spoon
   3 pieces of sponge
   scissors
   paper towels

For the students:
   script
   student pages

Background Information
The digestive system produces the chemicals used to break down food into nutrients that build and nourish the body's cells and provide the energy needed to sustain life. Digestion begins in the mouth and ends with the release of the body's solid waste.

In this activity, students place a peanut butter and jelly sandwich in a plastic bag and "process" the sandwich through the sections and organs of the digestive system.

Key Vocabulary
Bolus: a soft mass of chewed food that passes easily into the esophagus

Bicarbonate: the chemical (HCO_3) produced in the pancreas to neutralize stomach acid

Chyme: the mass of partly digested food passed by the stomach into the duodenum

Common bile duct: digestive chemicals from the liver and gallbladder enter the duodenum through this duct

Digestion: the mechanical and chemical process that breaks down food and drink so that the body can use the nutrients for growth and energy and eliminate the unused materials

Duodenum: the 25-centimeter long section of the small intestine that accepts chyme from the stomach and digestive chemicals from the common bile duct and the pancreatic duct

Feces: the body's solid waste products that are eliminated from the body through the anus

Gallbladder: stores the digestive chemicals produced in the liver until needed in the duodenum

Hydrochloric acid: the very strong acid produced in the stomach to digest food

Lower esophageal sphincter: ring-like muscle that opens and closes and allows chewed food (bolus) to pass into the stomach

Pancreas: produces digestive chemicals, one of which is bicarbonate

Pancreatic duct: digestive chemicals (including bicarbonate) enter the duodenum through this duct

Pyloric sphincter: ring-like muscle that opens and closes and allows chyme to enter the duodenum

Saliva: moistens food and helps to create a bolus that can be easily swallowed

Stomach: adds hydrochloric acid and digestive chemicals to food to change it into chyme

Management

1. Make a peanut butter and jelly sandwich on one piece of bread. Fold the bread in half and cut the sandwich into bite-size pieces. Store the pieces in a plastic bag until it's time to do the activity.
2. Cut a sponge into cubes. The activity needs about three cubes. Gather scissors, paper towels, marbles, plastic bags and labels (included), three 9-oz plastic cups, a plastic spoon, and the toilet lid page cutout.
3. Prepare condiments cups as follows: three filled with water, one filled with vinegar, and one half-filled with baking soda.
4. Copy the *Bag Labels* page and tape the labels to recloseable plastic bags as shown in this diagram.

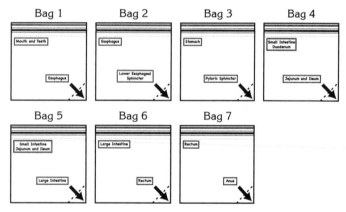

5. Twenty students are needed to take part in modeling how the digestive system digests a peanut butter and jelly sandwich. See *The Adventures of PB & J Bags* page. Assign students to bag groups.
6. The script can be read by one student or different students with one reading verses for each bag. If different students are used, nine readers will be needed.
7. At times, the contents of any bag can get messy. Be sure to have plenty of paper towels on hand for quick and easy clean up.

Procedure

1. Ask the *Key Question* and state the *Learning Goals*. Review or introduce the human digestive system and the *Key Vocabulary*.

2. Organize the students into bag groups and script readers. Have the bag groups form an ordered line, beginning with the *Mouth and Teeth* group.
3. Instruct the students to gather the supplies that are needed by each group. Have them refer to *The Adventures of PB & J Bags* page.
4. Discuss the procedure in which students in the bag groups will perform their roles as defined on the bag sheet while the script readers read each part.
5. To better coordinate the skit, rehearse one or two times without using the peanut butter sandwich and other supplies. Discuss the various organs and their functions during the rehearsals.
6. Perform the skit as directed.
7. Have students answer the questions on their student pages and conclude by discussing the *Connecting Learning* questions.

Connecting Learning

1. What role in the simulation did the marbles in the *Mouth and Teeth* bag play? [They simulated teeth.]
2. What did the water added to the *Mouth and Teeth* bag simulate? [saliva]
3. Describe a bolus. [a soft mass of chewed food]
4. In what part of the digestive system will you find hydrochloric acid? [stomach]
5. What does the acid do? [It helps to break down the food into smaller particles.]
6. What is the watery mass of partly digested food that leaves the stomach and enters the duodenum called? [chyme]
7. What important chemical is add to the chyme in the duodenum? [bicarbonate]
8. What happens to the chyme as it leaves the duodenum and continues on through the rest of the small intestine? [Nutrients are absorbed through the walls of the intestine into the blood and are carried to all parts of the body.]
9. What is the material that leaves the large intestine through the anus called? [feces]
10. What was the most interesting thing you learned from this activity?
11. What do you think would happen if your stomach quit adding acid to your food?
12. What kind of foods would you need to eat if you had no teeth? [soft foods] Why? [so they could be swallowed]
13. What are you wondering now?

Internet Connections

KidsHealth®

http://kidshealth.org/kid/htbw/

Select the stomach from the scrolling list for information on the stomach and digestive system, diagrams, movies, and more.

The Adventures of PB & J

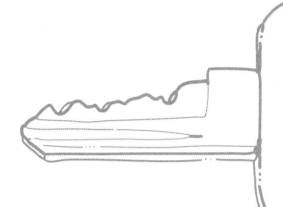

Key Question

What happens to a peanut butter and jelly sandwich as it passes through the digestive system?

Learning Goals

Students will:

- learn the major digestive organs and their functions, and

- perform a skit to model how food is processed through the digestive system.

The Adventures of PB & J
Bag Labels

Bag 1
| Mouth and Teeth | Esophagus |

Bag 2
| Esophagus | Lower Esophageal Sphincter |

Bag 3
| Stomach | Pyloric Sphincter |

Bag 4
| Small Intestine Duodenum | Jejunum and Ileum |

Bag 5
| Small Intestine Jejunum and Ileum | Large Intestine |

Bag 6
| Large Intestine | Rectum |

Bag 7
| Rectum | Anus |

The Adventures of PB & J
Bags

Mouth and Teeth Bag (4 students)

Student 1: Add three marbles and the bite-size pieces of peanut butter and jelly sandwich.

Student 2: Add one condiment cup of water to the sandwich.

Student 3: Knead the bag to form a bolus.

Student 4: Cut off the corner of the bag and squeeze the bolus into the *Esophagus* bag. (Keep the marbles in the *Mouth and Teeth* bag.)

Esophagus Bag (2 students)

Student 1: Receive the contents and close the bag. Move the bolus down the esophagus by encircling the bag with your fingers and squeezing so the bolus moves down toward the exit corner.

Student 2: Cut off the corner of the bag and squeeze the bolus into the *Stomach* bag.

Stomach Bag (3 students)

Student 1: Receive the contents. Add the cup of vinegar to the bolus. Close the bag.

Student 2: Knead the bag to mix the contents, forming chyme.

Student 3: Cut off the corner of the bag and squeeze the chyme into the *Duodenum* bag.

Small Intestine—Duodenum Bag (5 students)

Student 1: Receive the contents. Add a cup of water to the chyme to represent juice from the gallbladder.

Student 2: Add a cup of water to the chyme to represent juice from the liver.

Student 3: Add the baking soda to represent bicarbonate from the pancreas. Close the bag.

Student 4: Knead the bag to mix the contents.

Student 5: Cut the corner of the bag and squeeze the material into the *Jejunum and Ileum* bag.

Small Intestine—Jejunum and Ileum Bag (2 students)

Student 1: Receive the contents. Remove two or three spoons of liquid material from the bag to represent the absorption of nutrients in the jejunum and ileum. (Put the removed material in a plastic cup.) Close the bag.

Student 2: Cut the corner of the bag and squeeze the material into the *Large Intestine* bag.

Large Intestine Bag (2 students)

Student 1: Receive the contents. Add three pieces of sponge to the bag and gently squeeze so that sponges can absorb some of the liquid. Close the bag.

Student 2: Cut the corner of the bag and squeeze the material into the *Rectum/Anus* bag, leaving the sponges in the *Large Intestine* bag.

Rectum/Anus Bag (2 students)

Student 1: Receive the contents and close the bag.

Student 2: Place the *Toilet Lid* page on the table. Place a 9-oz plastic cup in the space indicated. Cut the corner of the bag and squeeze the material out.

The Adventures of PB & J
Script

Introduction
Come journey with me on a sort of spree
In a process each day we encounter.

It starts in the mouth and ends no doubt
In a place that you well will remember.

From table to mouth, I just need to shout
You are invited to bite and savor.

Mouth and Teeth Bag
Saliva and teeth form a bolus complete
In the esophagus it now enters.

Esophagus Bag
The muscles propel the bolus so well
To the stomach for quite an adventure.

Stomach Bag
The stomach it churns the muscles within
To break down the bolus even further.

The acids galore change food we adore
Into chyme that is liquidy matter.

Small Intestine—Duodenum Bag
The intestine small, as you may recall,
Does a job that's an absolute wonder.

Acid now altered, neutral is offered
To nourish our whole body's great structure.

Small Intestine—Jejunum and Ileum Bag
It absorbs the chyme; for cells it's mealtime,
An awesome feast for cellular pleasure.

Large Intestine Bag
Leftovers are passed—large intestine at last—
Where liquid is absorbed by our bodies.

Rectum/Anus Bag
The waste, there is some, goes to the rectum
Where it awaits for just the right moment.

Out of the anus, shhh, can you blame us?
This is surely a personal matter.

You ate what was good, the remainder it should
Be flushed for the story's now over.

Conclusion
The journey is through, and just to review
That your body was nourished and then some.

The rhyme is complete, so go to your seat
And finish the activity before you.

The Adventures of PB & J

Toilet Lid

place
cup
here

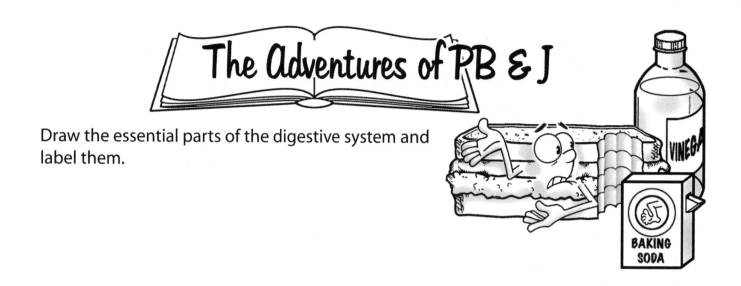

The Adventures of PB & J

Draw the essential parts of the digestive system and label them.

A peanut butter sandwich goes from a solid to a liquid to a solid through the process of digestion. Explain these different stages and where they occur.

Why does the body have to break down our food into very, very small particles?

What is the purpose of the hydrochloric acid in our stomach? (We used vinegar to model it.)

What is the purpose of the bicarbonate in the duodenum section of our small intestine? (We used baking soda to model it.)

The Adventures of PB & J

Connecting Learning

1. What role in the simulation did the marbles in the *Mouth and Teeth* bag play?

2. What did the water added to the *Mouth and Teeth* bag simulate?

3. Describe a bolus.

4. In what part of the digestive system will you find hydrochloric acid?

5. What does the acid do?

The Adventures of PB & J

Connecting Learning

6. What is the watery mass of partly digested food that leaves the stomach and enters the duodenum called?

7. What important chemical is add to the chyme in the duodenum?

8. What happens to the chyme as it leaves the duodenum and continues on through the rest of the small intestine?

9. What is the material that leaves the large intestine through the anus called?

The Adventures of PB & J

Connecting Learning

10. What was the most interesting thing you learned from this activity?

11. What do you think would happen if your stomach quit adding acid to your food?

12. What kind of foods would one need to eat if he/she had no teeth? Why?

13. What are you wondering now?

CHYME CHEMISTRY

Topic
Digestion

Key Question
What is one of the important digestive processes that happens in the section of the small intestine called the duodenum?

Learning Goals
Students will:
- model the one part of the process of digestion by simulating acidic chyme and the neutralizing chemical produced by the pancreas, and
- use a red cabbage indicator to test the pH of the simulated contents of the duodenum.

Guiding Documents
Project 2061 Benchmarks
- *From food, people obtain energy and materials for body repair and growth. The undigestible parts of food are eliminated.*
- *For the body to use food for energy and building materials, the food must first be digested into molecules that are absorbed and transported to cells.*
- *Like other animals, human beings have body systems for obtaining and providing energy, defense, reproduction, and the coordination of body functions.*

NRC Standard
- *The human organism has systems for digestion, respiration, reproduction, circulation, excretion, movement, control, and coordination, and for protection from disease. These systems interact with one another.*

Science
Life science
    human body
        digestive system
Physical science
    chemistry
        chemical reaction

Integrated Processes
Observing
Comparing and contrasting
Modeling
Generalizing

Materials
For the teacher:
    oatmeal, 19-oz container
    vinegar, 16-oz bottle
    baking soda
    red cabbage
    plastic cups, 9 oz
    condiment cups, 1 oz
    plastic coffee stir sticks

For each group:
    eyedropper
    paper towels

Background Information
The digestive system produces the chemicals used to break down food into nutrients that build and nourish the body's cells and provide the energy needed to sustain life. An overview of the digestive system describes the passage of food and drink, beginning in the mouth and ending with the release of the body's solid waste.

In this activity, students focus on one of the digestive processes that occurs in the partly digested food, called chyme, as it passes from the stomach, through the pyloric sphincter, into the duodenum. The duodenum is approximately 25 centimeters in length and is the upper portion of the small intestine. When the chyme first enters the duodenum, it is strongly acidic with a pH of approximately 2. The pancreas adds bicarbonate to the chyme through the pancreatic duct. By the time the chyme reaches the large intestine, its pH has been raised to a neutral 7.

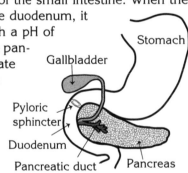

An *indicator* is a substance that changes color as an indication that two or more substances have chemically reacted. In this activity, students use red cabbage juice as an indicator to identify whether a substance is an acid or a base. This measure, called pH (potential of hydrogen), uses color and a scale from zero to fourteen.

Acidic						Neutral							Basic
pH 1	2	3	4	5	6	7	8	9	10	11	12	13	14
deep red	light red		red/purple				blue		blue/green		green	yellow/green	yellow
Strong				Weak		Neutral		Weak				Strong	

Students use red cabbage juice as a pH indicator to test a mixture of oatmeal and vinegar that simulates chyme. This mixture will test as acidic with a pH of approximately 2. Students then add a teaspoon of baking soda to the oatmeal-vinegar mixture. After the reaction between the vinegar and baking soda settles, students test the mixture, which now has a pH of approximately 7, which is neutral.

Key Vocabulary

Bicarbonate: the chemical (HCO_3) produced in the pancreas to neutralize stomach acid

Chemical change: a process that turns substances into other substances

Chyme: the mass of partly digested food passed by the stomach into the duodenum

Digestion: the mechanical and chemical processes that break down food and drink so that the body can use the nutrients for growth and energy

Duodenum: the 25-centimeter long section of the small intestine that accepts chyme from the stomach and digestive chemicals from the common bile duct and the pancreatic duct

Hydrochloric acid: the strong acid produced in the stomach to digest food

Pancreas: organ that produces digestive chemicals, one of which is bicarbonate

Pancreatic duct: digestive chemicals (including bicarbonate) enter the duodenum through this duct

pH: a measure of whether a substance is an acid, neutral, or a base

Pyloric sphincter: ring-like muscle that opens and closes and allows chyme to enter the duodenum

Stomach: digestive organ that adds hydrochloric acid and digestive chemicals to the food to change it into chyme

Management

1. To make the red cabbage indicator, add one cup of chopped red cabbage to three cups of water and place in a microwavable container. Cover the container and microwave on high for five minutes. Keep covered and let cool. When cooled, drain off and save the dark reddish-purple cabbage juice. Cabbage juice can be stored in the refrigerator for several days or for an extended period in the freezer.
2. Prepare the cups before doing the activity. Each group will need a condiment cup of red cabbage juice, vinegar (two-thirds full), and baking soda (one teaspoon). Each group will also need a 9-oz cup containing a teaspoon of dry oatmeal.
3. Schedule time to do the activity yourself. Doing so will help you better guide your students through the activity.
4. Eyedroppers (item number 1946) are available from AIMS.

Procedure

1. Review the human digestive system and the *Key Vocabulary*. Discuss the processes involved that break down our food into a usable form that can be absorbed by our bodies.
2. Ask the *Key Question* and state the *Learning Goals*. Distribute the student pages. Introduce or review the pH scale at the top of the first student page.
3. Distribute the cups (see *Management 3*), a plastic coffee stirrer, and an eyedropper to each group.
4. Have the students place the cups containing the oatmeal, vinegar, baking soda, and cabbage juice on the labeled circles on the first student page.
5. Tell the students to add the cup of white vinegar to the cup of oatmeal and use the coffee stirrer to mix the oats and vinegar.
6. Instruct the students to test the pH of the oats-vinegar mixture by adding three or four drops of the cabbage juice indicator to the mixture. Have them record the color, the approximate pH of the mixture, and their determination as to whether the pH of the mixture is acidic, neutral, or basic.
7. Now tell the students to add the cup of baking soda (sodium bicarbonate) to the cup of oats and vinegar and to use the stirrer to mix the oats, vinegar, and baking soda. Explain that one piece of evidence that a chemical change has taken place is the production of a gas as evidenced by the formation of bubbles.
8. Instruct the students to describe what happened.
9. Direct the students to test the pH of the oats-vinegar-baking soda mixture by adding three or four drops of red cabbage indicator to the mixture. Tell them to record the color and approximate pH of the mixture.
10. Have the students record whether the pH of the mixture is acidic, neutral, or basic.
11. Discuss how this activity modeled the parts of the digestive process.

Connecting Learning

1. In what part of the body does the digestive process begin? [the mouth]
2. What is the purpose of digestion? [to break down our food into a usable form]
3. What does a pH test tell us about a mixture? [whether a substance is an acid, neutral, or a base]
4. How does the pH of our food change as it goes through our digestive system? [Our food in our stomach becomes highly acidic with a pH around 2. In our duodenum, it is neutralized with a pH around 7.]
5. How do you know our food changed pH? [There was a color change when we tested it with the cabbage juice indicator.]

6. Why do you think our digestive system turns our food acidic? [Acids break down the food.]

7. Is chyme acidic, neutral, or basic as it enters the duodenum? [acidic]

8. What chemical does the pancreas add to the chyme? [bicarbonate]

9. What does this chemical do to the chyme? [raises its pH from acidic to neutral]

10. How is this activity like the real digestive process and how is it different? [In the real digestive process, hydrochloric acid is produced in the stomach that makes the chyme acidic. The pancreas adds bicarbonate (HCO_3) to the chyme to raise its pH to neutral. In the activity, white vinegar is used to represent stomach acid and baking soda (sodium bicarbonate—$NaHCO_3$) is used to neutralize the acidic vinegar.]

11. What are you wondering now?

Internet Connections
KidsHealth®
http://kidshealth.org/kid/htbw/
Select the stomach from the scrolling list for information on the stomach and digestive system, diagrams, movies, and more.

CHYME CHEMISTRY

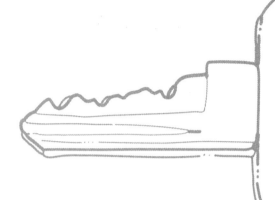

Key Question

What is one of the important digestive processes that happens in the section of the small intestine called the duodenum?

Learning Goals

- model one part of the process of digestion by simulating acidic chyme and the neutralizing chemical produced by the pancreas, and

- use a red cabbage indicator to test the pH of the simulated contents of the duodenum.

CHYME CHEMISTRY

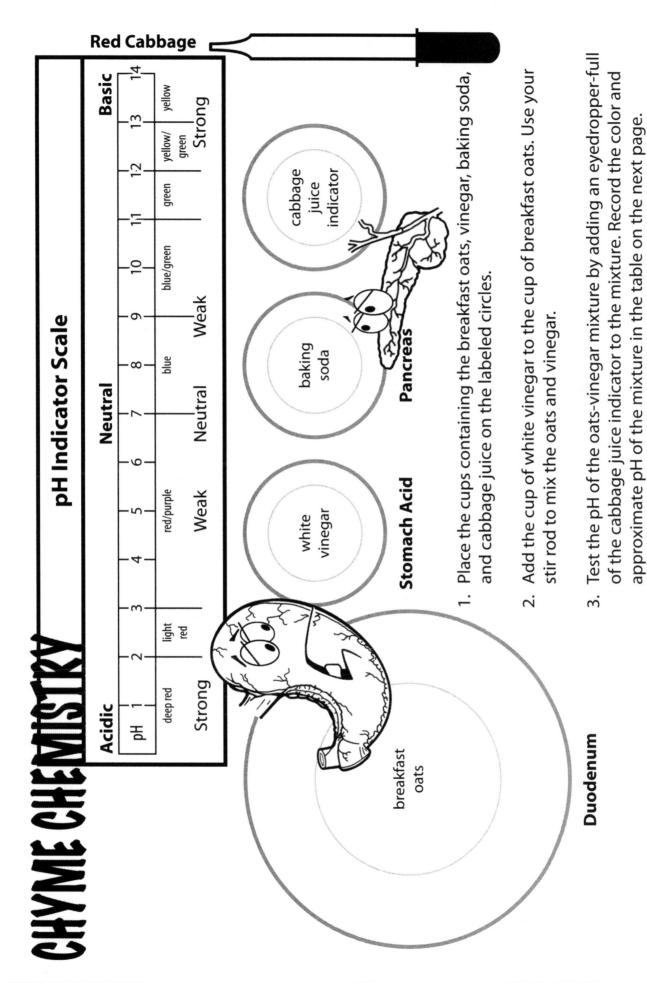

pH Indicator Scale

Red Cabbage

Acidic				Neutral					Basic			
pH	1	2	3	4	5	6	7	8	9	10	11	12	13	14

deep red — light red — red/purple — blue — blue/green — green — yellow/green — yellow

Strong — Weak — Neutral — Weak — Strong

Stomach Acid — white vinegar

Pancreas — baking soda — cabbage juice indicator

Duodenum — breakfast oats

1. Place the cups containing the breakfast oats, vinegar, baking soda, and cabbage juice on the labeled circles.

2. Add the cup of white vinegar to the cup of breakfast oats. Use your stir rod to mix the oats and vinegar.

3. Test the pH of the oats-vinegar mixture by adding an eyedropper-full of the cabbage juice indicator to the mixture. Record the color and approximate pH of the mixture in the table on the next page.

4. Is the pH of the mixture acidic, neutral, or basic?

CHYME CHEMISTRY

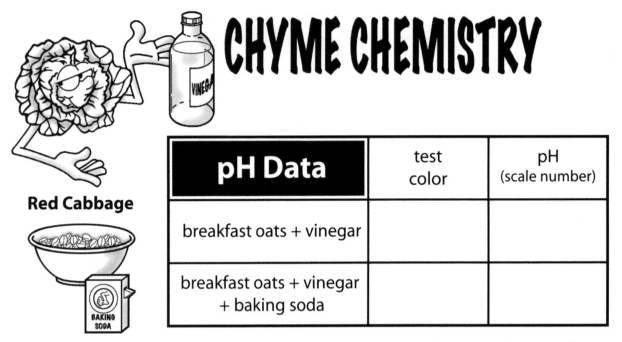

Red Cabbage

pH Data	test color	pH (scale number)
breakfast oats + vinegar		
breakfast oats + vinegar + baking soda		

5. Add the cup of baking soda (sodium bicarbonate) to the cup of oats and vinegar. Use your stir rod to mix the oats and vinegar.
Describe what happened.

6. Test the pH of the oats-vinegar-baking soda mixture by adding an eyedropper-full of red cabbage indicator to the mixture. Record the color and approximate pH of the mixture in the table above.

7. Is the pH of the mixture acidic, neutral, or basic?

8. What chemical does the pancreas add to the chyme to neutralize its pH?

9. How is this activity like the real digestive process and how is it different?

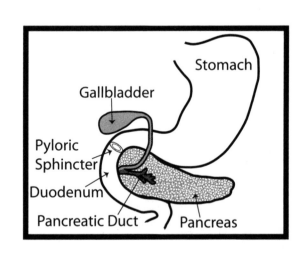

CHYME CHEMISTRY

Connecting Learning

1. In what part of the body does the digestive process begin?

2. What is the purpose of digestion?

3. What does a pH test tell us about a mixture?

4. How does the pH of our food change as it goes through our digestive system?

5. How do you know our food changed pH?

6. Why do you think our digestive system turns our food acidic?

CHYME CHEMISTRY

Connecting Learning

7. Is chyme acidic, neutral, or basic as it enters the duodenum?

8. What chemical does the pancreas add to the chyme?

9. What does this chemical do to the chyme?

10. How is this activity like the real digestive process and how is it different?

11. What are you wondering now?

The Food Tube

Topic
Digestive system

Key Question
What is the length of your digestive tract?

Learning Goals
Students will:
- determine the lengths of their digestive tracts, and
- model their tracts on outlines of their bodies.

Guiding Documents
Project 2061 Benchmarks
- *For the body to use food for energy and building materials, the food must first be digested into molecules that are absorbed and transported to cells.*
- *Like other animals, human beings have body systems for obtaining and providing energy, defense, reproduction, and the coordination of body functions.*
- *Length can be thought of as unit lengths joined together, area as a collection of unit squares, and volume as a set of unit cubes.*

NRC Standard
- *The human organism has systems for digestion, respiration, reproduction, circulation, excretion, movement, control, and coordination, and for protection from disease. These systems interact with one another.*

NCTM Standards 2000*
- *Understand such attributes as length, area, weight, volume, and size of angle and select the appropriate type of unit for measuring each attribute*
- *Select and apply appropriate standard units and tools to measure length, area, volume, weight, time, temperature, and the size of angles*

Math
Measurement
   length
Estimation
Computation
Proportional reasoning

Science
Life science
   human body
      digestive system

Integrated Processes
Observing
Collecting and recording data
Comparing and contrasting
Generalizing

Materials
Bulletin board paper
Crepe paper streamers
Metric tape measures
Glue
Construction paper
Scissors
Student pages

Background Information
The digestive tract is the body's passageway through which food moves and digests. The digestive tract, also called the alimentary canal, is a continuous muscular tube that extends from the mouth to the anus. It includes the mouth, esophagus, stomach, small intestine, large intestine, and the anus. Contributing organs are the salivary glands, pancreas, liver, and gallbladder.

The task of the digestive system is the physical and chemical breakdown of food to supply the body with its energy and nutrient needs for growth and repair.

There are several analogies that help us understand the digestive tract. One compares the digestive tract to a doughnut hole. The doughnut's hole is in the center and there is protective crust all around. Likewise, the digestive tract is a hole that runs from the mouth to the anus. The tube itself protects the body's interior from things external to it. There is no opening along the tube through which substances can enter the body. Substances can only enter the body when they are broken into pieces small enough that they can pass through the walls of the tube and enter the bloodstream.

Another analogy is that of an assembly line. Along the digestive tract, teeth physically break down the food and muscles move it through the passage to different "stations." Along the way, various stations of the digestive tract produce enzymes that aid in the chemical breakdown of food. The food is finally absorbed and waste products are collected and expelled.

The length of time involved in this assembly-line process varies from individual to individual. However, it is safe to say that the food must stay at each station along the way long enough for that station's job to be completed, whether that is the breakdown of carbohydrates, the breakdown of fats, the absorption of water, etc. Some approximate station times are: Mouth—less than one minute; Esophagus—a couple of seconds; Stomach—two to four hours; Small Intestine—one to four hours; Large Intestine—10 hours to several days.

An adult's digestive tract is approximately nine meters (30 ft) in length, or about five times the adult's height. In this activity, students will gain an appreciation of the length of the digestive tract and, if appropriate, begin to understand why its great length is necessary.

Management

1. Students will use traced body outlines on which to glue their digestive tracts. One outline per group is needed.
2. This activity is designed to be used at several levels. The simplest level is the measurement and placement of the digestive tract on the body cutout, and the identification of the major components. The most difficult level includes the placement, identification, and functional description of the components, including the contributing organs involved in the digestive process. You are encouraged to adapt this experience to meet your needs.
3. If the tracing of the students' bodies presents a management problem in the classroom, send some bulletin board paper home with a student from each group along with parental instructions to trace around their child's body.
4. Because the crepe paper color tends to run when glued, it is advisable to use light-colored streamers such as pink or yellow.
5. Use a paper cutter or scissors to cut the crepe paper streamers in half. These narrower streamers represent the small intestine, mouth, and esophagus. Use the full width to represent the large intestine.
6. Metric tape measures (item number 1926) are available from AIMS.

Procedure

1. Ask students how they think the food we eat nourishes our bodies. Discuss the fact that food must be broken down into a small enough size before it can be used by the body. Inform them that they will be exploring the digestive tract, or the passage the food takes from the moment it enters the mouth until it is excreted.

2. Have students get in groups of three. Distribute the bulletin board paper and have each group trace around one member's body. (See *Management 3.*)
3. Ask the *Key Question*. Write students' responses on the board.
4. Distribute the student page and the materials. Encourage students to follow the instructions to determine the lengths of their digestive tracts and create their models. (Students will be amazed at how much they have to "scrunch up" the small intestine to fit it in the appropriate space. Use this as a teaching opportunity to discuss the reason for its long length.)
5. Distribute the appropriate information page describing the digestive tract. Discuss the parts of the digestive system and their functions.

Connecting Learning

1. What is the function of the digestive system?
2. Approximately how long is your digestive tract?
3. About how many times longer is your digestive tract than your height? (You may want to have students cut a length of string equal to the length they have determined for their digestive tract. Using the string, they can concretely compare its length to the length of their body cutouts. Sample answers may be: "My digestive tract is over four times as long as my height, but less than five times." or "My digestive tract is four and three-fourths the length of my height.")
4. How does the length of your digestive tract compare to that of another student's? How can you explain the difference? [The other student is taller (or shorter) than I am.]
5. What is the longest component of the digestive tract? [the small intestine] Why do you think it is called the "small" intestine? [Its diameter is less than that of the large intestine.]
6. How were you able to fit the small intestine into place? [by wrinkling it up]
7. Why do you think the small intestine is so long?
8. How is this model like the real thing? How is it different?
9. What are you wondering now?

Extensions

1. Correlate the various digestive enzymes with the organs that produce them.
2. Have students determine the average ratio of their heights to the length of their digestive tracts. Have them apply this ratio to a professional basketball player whose height they know.

* Reprinted with permission from *Principles and Standards for School Mathematics,* 2000 by the National Council of Teachers of Mathematics. All rights reserved.

The Food Tube

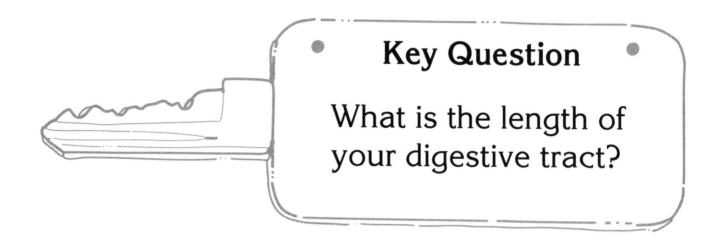

Key Question

What is the length of your digestive tract?

Learning Goals

Students will:

- determine the lengths of their digestive tracts, and

- model their tracts on outlines of their bodies.

The Food Tube

How long is your digestive tract?

Key
Mouth = 10 cm
Esophagus = 25 cm
Stomach = 15 cm
Small intestine = Height x 3
Large intestine = Height + 15 cm

You need:

Body outline   Glue   Scissors
Construction paper   Metric tape measure
Crepe paper streamers (narrow and wide)

Do this:

1. Find and record the height of your group's model. ⬜ cm

2. Use the key to calculate the length of the digestive tract from the mouth to the top of the stomach. Cut a length of narrow crepe paper that is this long.

3. Cut a stomach from construction paper that is the right size. Glue the mouth, esophagus, and stomach in place on the body outline.

4. Calculate the length of the digestive tract so far (from the mouth to the end of the stomach). ⬜ cm

5. Determine the length of the small intestine. Cut a length of narrow crepe paper that is this long. ⬜ cm

6. Determine the length of the large intestine to the anus. Cut a length of wide crepe paper that is this long. ⬜ cm

7. Glue the small and large intestine in place on the body outline. Use the diagram to help you.

8. Find the total length of the digestive tract. ⬜ cm

9. On your body cutout, label the mouth, esophagus, stomach, small intestine, large intestine, and anus.

How many times longer is the digestive tract than your model's height?

On the back of this paper, explain how you determined this.

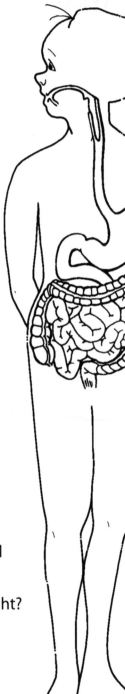

The Food Tube

Mouth
The teeth physically break the food into smaller bits. The tongue helps to move the food particles into a ball that is then swallowed.

Esophagus
Once the food has been swallowed, it moves down the throat into the esophagus. The esophagus is lined with muscles that help to mix the food and push it down toward the stomach.

Stomach
The stomach is a J-shaped expansion of the digestive tube that can hold two to four liters of food! The stomach stores food. Its muscles knead the food, breaking it down even more. The stomach adds chemicals to the food that turn the food into a soupy liquid.

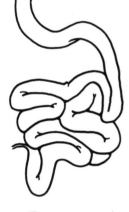

Small Intestine
The soupy liquid moves into the small intestine, a narrow tube (two to four cm in diameter)—the longest portion of the digestive tract. Here the food is broken down into small enough particles that it can be absorbed into the bloodstream.

Large Intestine
Undigested food is passed into the large intestine. Water and salt are absorbed by the large intestine. The undigested food, dead cells, and dead bacteria left in the large intestine are called feces. Muscles in the large intestine move the feces on toward the anus.

Anus
The anus is the exit point for the feces. The anus has strong muscles that, when relaxed, allow the body to get rid of its solid waste.

The Food Tube

Mouth
The teeth physically break the food into smaller bits. The tongue helps to move the food particles into a ball that is then swallowed.

Esophagus
Once the food has been swallowed, it moves down the throat into the esophagus. The esophagus is lined with muscles that help to mix the food and push it down toward the stomach.

Stomach
The stomach is a J-shaped expansion of the digestive tube that can hold two to four liters of food! The stomach stores food. Its muscles knead the food, breaking it down even more. The stomach adds chemicals to the food that turns the food into a soupy liquid.

Small Intestine
The soupy liquid moves into the small intestine, a narrow tube (two to four cm in diameter)—the longest portion of the digestive tract. Here the food is broken down into small enough particles that it can be absorbed into the bloodstream.

Large Intestine
Undigested food is passed on into the large intestine. Water and salt is absorbed by the large intestine. The undigested food, dead cells, and dead bacteria left in the large intestine are called feces. Muscles in the large intestine move the feces on toward the anus.

Anus

The anus is the exit point for the feces. The anus has strong muscles that, when relaxed, allow the body to get rid of its solid waste.

Salivary Glands
The salivary glands produce saliva that starts the chemical breakdown of carbohydrates. Saliva also moistens the food making it easier to swallow.

Liver
The liver is an organ about the size of a football. It removes harmful substances and waste products from the blood. The liver produces bile that acts like a detergent in breaking up fats. The liver stores the fats and carbohydrates we use for energy along with iron and other vitamins. It regulates the blood sugar levels in the body.

Pancreas
The pancreas produces chemicals that help in the digestion of carbohydrates, fats, and proteins. It also produces a chemical that helps to neutralize the stomach acids.

Gallbladder
The gallbladder stores the bile that was produced by the liver. The gallbladder releases the bile into the small intestine where it helps to break down the fats we have eaten.

The Food Tube

Connecting Learning

1. What is the function of the digestive system?

2. Approximately how long is your digestive tract?

3. About how many times longer is your digestive tract than your height?

4. How does the length of your digestive tract compare to that of another student's?

5. What is the longest component of your digestive tract? Why do you think it is called the "small" intestine?

The Food Tube

Connecting Learning

6. How were you able to fit the small intestine into place?

7. Why do you think the small intestine is so long?

8. How is this model like the real thing? How is it different?

9. What are you wondering now?

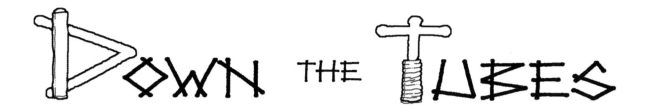

Down the Tubes

Topic
Digestive system

Key Question
How does the design of the small intestine help in the digestive process?

Learning Goals
Students will:
- explore surface area concepts, and
- apply surface area concepts to the small intestine.

Guiding Documents
Project 2061 Benchmarks
- *From food, people obtain energy and materials for body repair and growth. The indigestible parts of food are eliminated.*
- *For the body to use food for energy and building materials, the food must first be digested into molecules that are absorbed and transported to cells.*
- *Like other animals, human beings have body systems for obtaining and providing energy, defense, reproduction, and the coordination of body functions.*

NRC Standard
- *The human organism has systems for digestion, respiration, reproduction, circulation, excretion, movement, control, and coordination, and for protection from disease. These systems interact with one another.*

NCTM Standard 2000*
- *Understand such attributes as length, area, weight, volume, and size of angle and select the appropriate type of unit for measuring each attribute*

Math
Measurement
    surface area

Science
Life science
    human body
        digestive system
            small intestine

Integrated Processes
Observing
Comparing and contrasting
Applying

Materials
For each student:
    2 paper-wrapped drinking straws
    metric ruler
    transparent tape or glue
    chenille stem (see *Extension*)

Background Information
The small intestine is named not for its length (approximately 2.75 meters in adults) but for its diameter (between 2–4 cm). The size of the small intestine may not seem too amazing until the folds and small finger-like projections called villi (and microvilli) are taken into consideration. They increase the small intestine's surface area to about 300 m^2, the size of a tennis court!

In this activity, students will measure the surface area of the paper wrapping from a drinking straw. They will then scrunch the paper from another drinking straw, and be guided into the realization that the surface area has remained the same even though the scrunched paper now takes up less space. Application will be made to the fact that the folds and scrunching of the small intestine allow for a great deal of surface area for the absorption of nutrients.

Management
1. When students measure the surface area of the paper wrappers, have them measure from the inside of the glued edge to the fold and multiply by two to accommodate for the front and back of the paper. They will then multiply this width measure by the length measure. Another method would be to multiply the length and width of the front side and the back side and add the two products together.
2. The drinking straws will not actually be used in the activity. When the activity is over, have students place the unused straws in the science equipment area or some other designated area where they will be available for future use.
3. Metric rulers (item number 1909) are available from AIMS.

Procedure

1. Ask the *Key Question* and state the *Learning Goals*.
2. Tell students that they will be comparing paper wrappers from drinking straws to the design of the small intestine.
3. Distribute the first paper-wrapped drinking straw, a ruler, and the student page to each student.
4. Tell students to open the top end of the wrapper and gently slip the straw out it. Ask them to place the wrappers on their desks and smooth them out as much as possible.
5. Ask students how they could determine the surface area for the paper wrapper. (See suggestions in *Management 1.*) Have them measure and record the information on the student page.
6. Distribute the second paper-wrapped drinking straw to each student.
7. Tell them that this time they will open the top end of the wrapper and scrunch the paper down the straw. Have them leave the paper scrunched.
8. Instruct them to record the measurements on the student page. Be sure that students realize that the surface area of the straw wrapper is still the same. The scrunched one just takes up less length because of all the little folds.
9. Invite students to glue (or tape) their smooth wrapper lengths together end to end and measure the total length.
10. Have them glue (or tape) the scrunched wrappers together end to end, working as best they can to keep them scrunched. Direct them to measure this length.
11. Discuss what they learned and how the scrunched straw wrappers are similar to the small intestine.

Connecting Learning

1. How did you determine the surface area of the paper wrapper?
2. Why did you have to consider the width twice? [to include both the front and back of the wrapper]
3. How can you explain that the surface area of the smooth wrapper and the scrunched wrapper are the same? [The scrunched wrapper has the same length and width, but it was pushed down so that it has lots of folds.]
4. How is the scrunched wrapper like the small intestine? [They both have lots of folds.]
5. Why do you think this would be a good design for the small intestine?
6. Can you think of other things that are scrunched for a reason? What are they?
7. What are you wondering now?

Extension

Distribute the chenille stems. Relate the bristles to the villi in the small intestine. Discuss how the villi add even more surface area to the small intestine and aid in the absorption of nutrients.

* Reprinted with permission from *Principles and Standards for School Mathematics*, 2000 by the National Council of Teachers of Mathematics. All rights reserved.

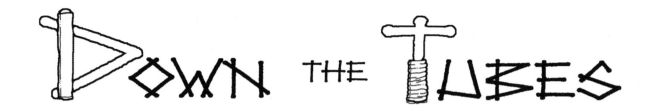

DOWN THE TUBES

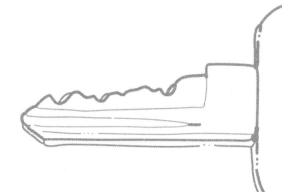

Key Question

How does the design of the small intestine help in the digestive process?

Learning Goals

Students will:

- explore surface area concepts, and

- apply surface area concepts to the small intestine.

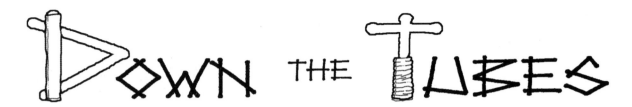

DOWN THE TUBES

USE STRAW ONE

Tear open the end of the wrapper and remove the straw. Determine the surface area of your wrapper. Show your work.

USE STRAW TWO

Tear open the end of the wrapper and scrunch the paper down. Remove the straw.

1. What has changed about the wrapper?

2. What has stayed the same?

Length of ⬚ = _____ cm. Glue or tape all the ⬚ together. Total Length = _____ cm

Length of ⬚ = _____ cm. Glue or tape all the ⬚ together. Total Length = _____ cm

The inside of the small intestine has many folds. How is the small intestine like the straw wrapper you scrunched?

Why do you think it is designed this way?

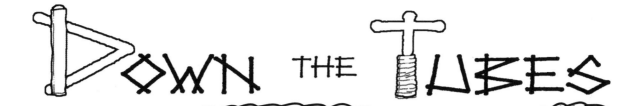

Down the Tubes

Connecting Learning

1. How did you determine the surface area of the paper wrapper?

2. Why did you have to consider the width twice?

3. How can you explain that the surface area of the smooth wrapper and the scrunched wrapper are the same?

4. How is the scrunched wrapper like the small intestine?

5. Why do you think this would be a good design for the small intestine?

6. Can you think of other things that are scrunched for a reason? What are they?

7. What are you wondering now?

Topic
Digestive system

Key Question
How does the food we eat nourish all parts of our bodies?

Learning Goals
Students will:
- observe the passing of materials through a membrane, and
- relate this process to digestion in the small intestine.

Guiding Documents
Project 2061 Benchmarks
- *From food, people obtain energy and materials for body repair and growth. The indigestible parts of food are eliminated.*
- *For the body to use food for energy and building materials, the food must first be digested into molecules that are absorbed and transported to cells.*
- *Like other animals, human beings have body systems for obtaining and providing energy, defense, reproduction, and the coordination of body functions.*

NRC Standard
- *The human organism has systems for digestion, respiration, reproduction, circulation, excretion, movement, control, and coordination, and for protection from disease. These systems interact with one another.*

Science
Life science
  human body
    digestive system

Integrated Processes
Observing
Comparing and contrasting
Applying

Materials
For each group:
  sausage casing, 25 cm (see *Management 2*)
  string
  water
  food coloring
  corn syrup
  container such as liter box

Background Information
The human digestive system is basically a tube running through the body. The digestive tract is composed of several compartments that both physically and chemically break down the food we eat so that it can be absorbed by individual cells. This activity simulates the absorption of nutrients that occurs in the small intestine. The small intestine is the first point at which the foods we have eaten actually enter the body.

Digestion begins as soon as the food enters the mouth and comes in contact with the teeth and saliva. As the food progresses through the digestive tract, it becomes smaller and smaller. However, it is in the small intestine that food is broken down into parts so small that they can pass through the walls of the intestine. Through the process of absorption, the nutrients then diffuse out of the intestinal cells into the blood stream where they are carried by the blood to all the body cells, some 40 trillion in all.

This activity utilizes sausage casing to simulate the small intestine. Because the walls of the sausage casing are so thin, water will pass through the membrane. Application should be made to the nutrients being absorbed into the blood stream.

Management
1. This activity should follow some more introductory-type activities dealing with the digestive system.
2. Sausage casing can be obtained from a meat market or the meat section of some grocery stores. Each group will need about 25 cm (the approximate length of the duodenum, the portion of the small intestine where most digestion occurs). If natural sausage casing is used, the students will notice that water begins to pass through as soon as they fill the casing. (Do not buy plastic casing, as it is impermeable.)

3. Add food coloring to the water to make it more visible, both in the casing and after it has passed from the membrane. The corn syrup is used for increasing the rate of osmosis and for dramatic effect; the diffused water is easily visible floating on top of the corn syrup.
4. If desired, add red food coloring to the corn syrup so students can more easily relate it to blood.
5. Containers need to be large enough that the water-filled casing can be covered with corn syrup. Liter boxes work well. Liter boxes are available from AIMS (item number 1913).
6. When finished with the activity, have students empty the contents of their containers into a large zipper-type bag. Give the bag to a custodian for proper disposal.

Procedure

1. Ask the *Key Question* and state the *Learning Goals*.
2. Show the students the sausage casing. Direct them to use a piece of string to tightly tie one end of the casing.
3. Have them fill the casing with colored water to within 4–5 cm of the top and tie the top. Tell them to place the filled casing in the bottom of the container. Relate the liquid state in the filled casing to the food in our body as it is digested in the small intestine.
4. Have students add corn syrup to cover the filled casing. Ask them to predict what will happen.
5. Set the simulations aside for an hour or more.
6. Have students observe what has happened to the filled casing. Encourage them to lift the casing out of the corn syrup to better see the results. Discuss how this is like digestion in the small intestine.

Connecting Learning

1. What happened to the liquid in the casing?
2. Why do you think this happened?
3. How is this simulation like digestion in our small intestines?
4. Why do our intestines have folds and villi?
5. How do the food nutrients get to all of our body cells?
6. What are you wondering now?

CASING THE SYSTEM

Key Question

How does the food we eat nourish all parts of our bodies?

Learning Goals

Students will:

- observe the passing of materials through a membrane, and

- relate this process to digestion in the small intestine.

CASING THE SYSTEM

Draw and label how you set up this experiment.

What happened?

How is this like the digestion that happens in our small intestines?

Connecting Learning

1. What happened to the liquid in the casing?

2. Why do you think this happened?

3. How is this simulation like digestion in our small intestines?

4. Why do our intestines have folds and villi?

5. How do the food nutrients get to all of our body cells?

6. What are you wondering now?

Isn't It Interesting...
It Takes Guts

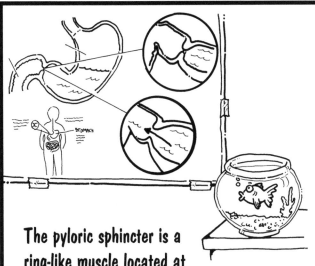

The pyloric sphincter is a ring-like muscle located at the end of the stomach. It opens to let little spurts of food into the small intestine. If you make your lips like a fish mouth, this is kind of how this muscle works.

The small intestine is divided into three parts: the duodenum, the jejunum, and the ileum. You'll impress your family if you can use those words in your dinner conversation!

When your stomach growls or gurgles, it's really the sound of gases, digestive juices, and food that is being digested and pushed through your stomach and intestines. The word for the growling sound is borborygmus!

As an adult, your intestines will probably be at least 8 meters (25 ft), but the length of a full-grown horse's intestines is just under 30 meters (89 ft).

TAKE ME TO THE CLEANERS

Topic
Urinary system

Key Questions
1. What do the kidneys do?
2. How does the bladder work?

Learning Goals
Students will:
- investigate how the kidneys remove waste products from the blood, and
- know that urine is stored in the bladder.

Guiding Documents
Project 2061 Benchmarks
- *From food, people obtain energy and materials for body repair and growth. The undigestible parts of food are eliminated.*
- *Cells continually divide to make more cells for growth and repair. Various organs and tissues function to serve the needs of cells for food, air, and waste removal.*

NRC Standard
- *The human organism has systems for digestion, respiration, reproduction, circulation, excretion, movement, control, and coordination, and for protection from disease. These systems interact with one another.*

Science
Life science
> human body
>> urinary system

Integrated Processes
Observing
Comparing and contrasting
Applying
Drawing conclusions

Materials
For the class:
> round or pear-shaped party balloon, 6-inch
>> (see *Management 1*)
> clear tape (see *Management 1*)
> container of vegetable juice, 1.5 oz or larger
>> (see *Management 3*)

For each student group:
> one plastic cup, 6 ounce or larger
> one small cup, any kind
> coffee filter or a sheet of paper towel
>> (see *Management 4*)
> rubber band

For each student:
> *Removing the Waste* rubber band book
> #19 rubber band
> student page

Background Information
The urinary system is made up of the kidneys, ureters, bladder, and urethra. It is responsible for ridding the body of water-soluble waste through the elimination of urine. As blood travels through the body, it delivers oxygen to cells and removes carbon dioxide and waste. When blood enters the kidneys through the renal artery, it is filtered by nephrons. These nephrons remove waste from the blood. This waste is combined with water to make urine. From the kidneys, the urine travels down the ureters to the bladder. The bladder is like a somewhat stretchy storage bag. On the bladder wall are stretch receptors. As the bladder fills and stretches, these receptors start signaling that it's time to go to the bathroom. The last step of the process is when the urine leaves the bladder and goes out of the body through a tube called the urethra.

Management
1. Inexpensive tape and balloons work best. Balloons recommended for helium use may be coated with a substance that prevents the tape from sticking. If you use those, wash with warm, soapy water and blot dry. Bargain clear tape usually works better than the "magic" variety. Masking tape may also work. Half-inch tape works better than wider tape.
2. Characteristics of both tape and balloons vary greatly. It is recommended that you try the bladder demonstration before doing it in class to be sure that it will work with the materials you plan to use.
3. Vegetable juice is particularly effective because of its color, but almost any unfiltered juice may be substituted, as may coffee with grounds added. Orange juice with pulp tends to clog the filter.

4. If you plan to use paper towels for filters, it is recommended you test them ahead of time. The super absorbent varieties do not work as well as the less expensive brands.
5. Inflate and deflate the balloon to stretch it out before beginning the demonstration.

Procedure

Part One

1. Ask the students what they already know about their kidneys and what they do. List their responses on the board. Distribute the rubber band book and direct them to read it.
2. Have the students go over the list of responses, correcting or adding to the information as needed.
3. Help the student locate their own kidneys:
   • stand with hands on hips and thumbs pointing backwards
   • slide hands up until they just touch the bottom of the ribcage
   • kidneys are located in area where thumbs are pointing (students will not be able to feel them).
4. Ask the students what substances they can think of that are filtered. [coffee, motor oil, some types of juice, the air, etc.] Guide them to understand the purpose of filtering. [to get rid of unwanted substances such as waste material or impurities; sometimes for a "clean" appearance]
5. Distribute a large empty cup, paper towel or coffee filter, and rubber band to each group. Demonstrate making a simple filter by covering the mouth of the cup with a paper towel or coffee filter and holding it in place with a rubber band. Be sure the filter is not stretched too tight. Direct the students to push down lightly on the center of the towel or filter so that the surface bows slightly down into the cup.

6. Give each group a cup containing a few ounces of unfiltered juice (see *Management 3*). Direct them to pour the juice slowly onto the filter so that juice flows through the filter into the cup. Ask them to observe what happens.
7. Have the students compare the juice before and after being filtered. Discuss, guiding the discussion to compare and contrast this model to the way our kidneys work.

Part Two

1. Hold up a balloon for the class to see. Explain that this balloon represents a bladder, the somewhat stretchy organ where the kidneys send urine to be stored.
2. Blow enough air into the balloon to make it about the size of a tennis ball. The latex should be stretched enough to hold its shape. Twist the neck to keep the air inside.
3. Use four strips of tape to make a couple of Xs at different locations on the balloon skin. Rub the tape to help it adhere as strongly as possible. Explain that the tape represents the *stretch receptors* on the wall of the bladder. Tell the students that this partially inflated balloon represents "Stage One"—the kidney is sending urine into the bladder, but it isn't stretched all that much, and the person probably is not even aware of it.
4. Puff a little bit more air into the balloon and watch the tape strain. You may see wrinkles around the tape, or the balloon may appear somewhat distorted. This is "Stage Two"—the receptors are being tugged, and it's becoming a bit uncomfortable. The person becomes aware of needing to urinate soon, and perhaps is wondering about whether to wait until recess.
5. Inflate the balloon slowly until the tape is about ready to give way. Point out the deformation of the balloon around the tape. The tape may look shiny from being stretched. This is "Stage Three," and the receptors are signaling: get to the bathroom NOW!
6. Slowly deflate the balloon. The tape on the outside will relax and wrinkle. The balloon is now as small and relaxed as it can get. Explain that a bladder also has a minimum size. The receptors can tell when the bladder is truly empty.
7. Encourage the students to discuss what they have observed.

Connecting Learning

1. What is the material left in the filter? [bits of fruit/vegetable used to make the juice.] Were you surprised by the amount left behind? Explain.
2. What do you think would happen if you filtered the juice a second and even a third time?
3. In what ways are your kidneys like this filter system? How are they different?
4. What do you think would happen if your bladder could not stretch?
5. Do you think the kidneys and bladder are as important as the heart? Explain.
6. What are you wondering now?

Extensions

1. Some people whose kidneys are diseased or do not work properly have their blood filtered artificially in a process known as *dialysis*. Do research to find out more about this lifesaving procedure.

2. It is now possible for people whose kidneys are failing to receive a transplanted kidney from someone else. There are often stories in the newspaper about people who give one of their healthy kidneys to someone who desperately needs one. Look on the Internet and in other reference materials to find out more about kidney transplants.

3. Plant cells produce waste material too, but they don't get rid of it. Instead they store it in a large *vacuole* in the middle of each cell. The vacuole is like a garbage dump that gradually fills up as the cell gets older. Research to learn more about this process.

Internet Connections

KidsHealth®
http://www.kidshealth.org/kid/htbw/
Select the kidneys or the bladder from the scrolling list for information on the urinary system, diagrams, movies, and more.

Curriculum Correlation

Literature

Cole, Joanna. *The Magic School Bus: Inside the Human Body*. Scholastic, Inc. New York. 1990.
Teacher and students travel through the human body.

Delafosse, Claude. *Human Body (First Discovery Book)*. Scholastic, Inc. New York. 2000.
Comes with a "magic paper flashlight" for the reader to use to explore different internal organs.

Walker, Richard, ed. *Encyclopedia of the Human Body*. DK Publishing. New York. 2002.
Detailed look at form and function of human body, plus nutrition, exercise, and the impact of modern technology in diagnosing and fighting disease.

FROM HEAD TO TOE

TAKE ME TO THE CLEANERS

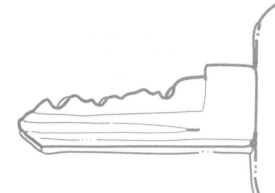

Key Questions

1. What do the kidneys do?

2. How does the bladder work?

Learning Goals

Students will:

- investigate how the kidneys remove waste products from the blood, and

- know that urine is stored in the bladder.

7

Your bladder is like a somewhat stretchy storage bag. On the bladder wall are *stretch receptors*. As the bladder fills and stretches, these receptors start signaling you that it's time to go to the bathroom. The last step of the process is when the urine leaves your bladder and goes out of your body through a tube called the *urethra*.

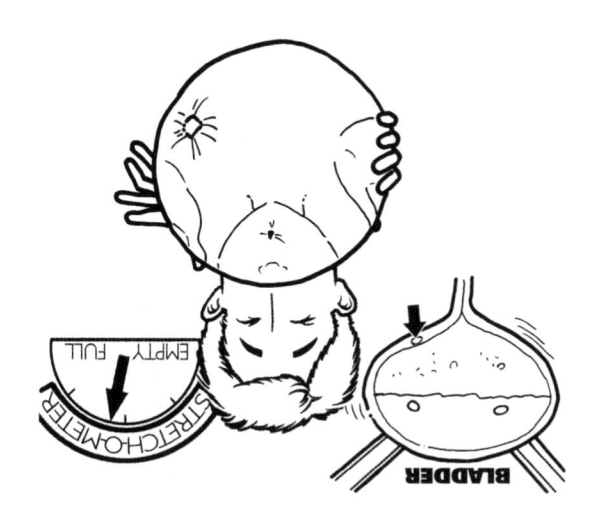

Take a look at the wastebasket in your classroom. It probably gets pretty full just about every day. As you and your classmates go about your activities, you produce a certain amount of trash.

Your cells, blood stream, kidneys, and bladder are at work all the time, even when you are sleeping. It's a good thing! Urine is a toxic waste. Without your *urinary* system, waste material would poison your cells and, before long, your entire body.

REMOVING the Waste

8

1

4

The cells in your body need to get rid of waste too. Since cells are so small, their waste material is in the form of molecules. Your blood picks up these waste molecules and carries them to your kidneys.

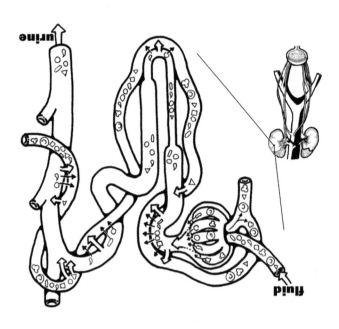

The main job of your kidneys is to filter the waste material out of your blood. Your kidneys are so important that you can't live without at least one of them. Fortunately, you have two. Each is about the size of a deck of cards.

What would it be like if that wastebasket never got emptied? After a while, it would really start piling up and getting in the way. It would also smell bad. Living with all that garbage certainly wouldn't be healthy.

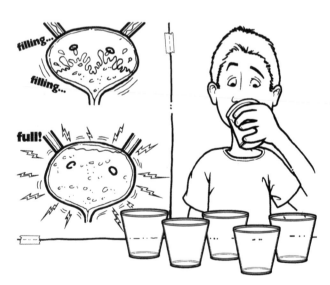

All that waste material doesn't stay in your kidneys. It is combined with water to form *urine*. Tubes called the *ureters* carry the urine—about six cups a day—to your *bladder*.

TAKE ME TO THE CLEANERS

Use words and drawings to describe what you did to filter the juice.

Explain how this model is similar to the way your kidneys work.

Connecting Learning

1. What is the material left in the filter? Were you surprised by the amount left behind? Explain.

2. What do you think would happen if you filtered the juice a second and even a third time?

3. In what ways are your kidneys like this filter system? How are they different?

4. What do you think would happen if your bladder could not stretch?

5. Do you think the kidneys and bladder are as important as the heart? Explain.

6. What are you wondering now?

Topic
Skeletal system

Key Question
What are the major bones in the human body, and how do they fit together?

Learning Goals
Students will:
- learn about the skeletal system and the major bones of the human body,
- cut out and assemble bones to make a model human skeleton, and
- label some of the bones.

Guiding Documents
Project 2061 Benchmark
- *Geometric figures, number sequences, graphs, diagrams, sketches, number lines, maps, and stories can be used to represent objects, events, and processes in the real world, although such representations can never be exact in every detail.*

NRC Standard
- *The human organism has systems for digestion, respiration, reproduction, circulation, excretion, movement, control, and coordination, and for protection from disease. These systems interact with one another.*

Science
Life science
    human body
        skeletal system

Integrated Processes
Observing
Comparing and contrasting

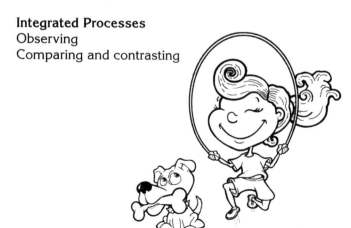

Materials
Dem Bones rubber band book
#19 rubber bands
Scissors
Tape
Bulletin board paper (see *Management 3*)
Markers
Student pages

Background Information
There are 206 bones in the adult human body. These bones comprise the skeletal system, which gives structure and protection to the body. The bones are also where blood cells are made. The skeletal system is organized into two "skeletons"—the axial skeleton and the appendicular skeleton. The axial skeleton is comprised of the skull, spine, ribs, and sternum. The remaining bones of the arms and legs, the pelvis, the clavicle, and the scapula are the appendicular skeleton.

Management
1. This activity is written for students to work in groups with each group creating one skeleton. If desired, you can have each student create his or her own skeleton.
2. Each group needs one set of bones.
3. Each group will need a piece of bulletin board paper on which to mount the skeleton model so that its parts can be labeled. If possible, use a light color other than white so that the model will contrast with the background, but the labels will still be easy to read.

Procedure
1. Distribute the *Dem Bones* rubber band book and #19 rubber bands to each student. Have students assemble the books.
2. Read through the information together as a class. Discuss new terminology and ask students if they already know the names and locations of some of their bones. Have them share what they know.
3. Distribute the page with the labeled skeleton to each group of students. Instruct them to use their fingers to locate their clavicles. Ask them what they feel. Can they detect where the clavicle meets the sternum? Have them run their hands along their backs. Can they feel the vertebrae in their spines?

4. Explain that each group will be cutting out pictures of the bones that make up the human body. They will work together, using the page they have just been given as a guide, to assemble all of the bones into a complete skeleton.

5. Distribute the bone pages, scissors, bulletin board paper, and tape to each group. Allow time for students to cut out the parts and tape them to the bulletin board paper using the paper showing the completed skeleton as a guide. Inform students that because of how the bones were grouped to cut apart, their model skeleton will not look exactly like the one on the page. For example, the clavicle goes in front of the rib cage to connect to the sternum, but because the clavicle is grouped with the shoulder blades, it must go behind the rib cage in the model.

6. When groups have completed the assembly, distribute markers. Instruct students to label the bones on their models as they are labeled on the page with the skeleton.

7. Display the skeletons in the room or in a hallway. To test students on the names of the bones, cover the labels with sticky notes, and have them identify the bones, then remove the labels to see if they are correct.

Connecting Learning

1. What is the purpose of the skeletal system? [It provides structure to our bodies and protects our internal organs. Bones also produce blood cells.]

2. How many bones would you guess are in your body right now? Justify your response. (Elementary students will have fewer than 300 but more than 206 bones in their bodies, as the fusing of bones is not completed until growth is completed.)

3. Where is your femur? ...your radius? ...your pelvis? ...your clavicle? ...etc.

4. How does your skeleton model compare to an actual skeleton? [two dimensional, doesn't show all the bones, smaller, etc.]

5. What are you wondering now?

Extensions

1. Study the connections between bones including flexions, ligaments, tendons, and joints.

2. Make a model that is connected with paper fasteners so that the hands, arms, feet, and legs can move and bend.

Internet Connections

KidsHealth®
http://www.kidshealth.org/kid/htbw/
Select the bone from the scrolling list for information on the bones, diagrams, movies, and more.

Curriculum Correlation

Clayman, Charles (Ed.). *The Human Body: An Illustrated Guide to Its Structure, Function, and Disorders.* Dorling Kindersley. New York. 1995.

Parker, Janet (Ed.). *The Human Body Atlas.* Chartwell Books. Edison, NJ. 2002.

Treays, Rebecca. *Understanding Your Muscles & Bones.* Usborne Publishing Ltd. London. 1997.

Dem Bones

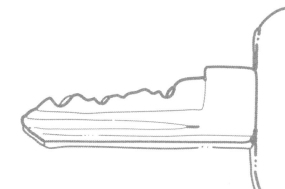

Key Question

What are the major bones in the human body, and how do they fit together?

Learning Goals

Students will:

- learn about the skeletal system and the major bones of the human body,

- cut out and assemble bones to make a model human skeleton, and

- label some of the bones.

The Appendicular skeleton

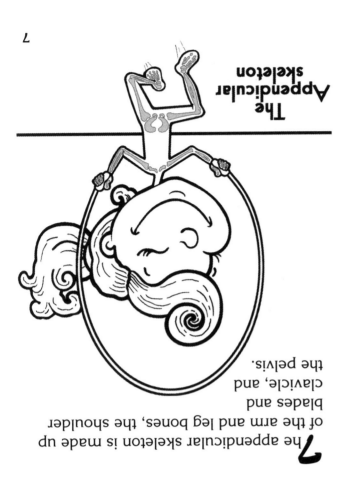

7 The appendicular skeleton is made up of the arm and leg bones, the shoulder blades and clavicle, and the pelvis.

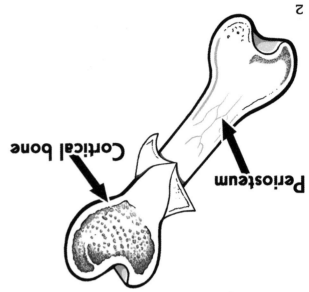

Cortical bone

Periosteum

Not every bone is exactly the same, but most have the same layers. The outside layer is called the periosteum. It contains nerves and blood vessels. Under that is a layer of hard bone (also called cortical bone). This is what you see when you look at a skeleton.

Use the diagram of the skeletal system to learn the names of some of the major bones in the body and their locations.

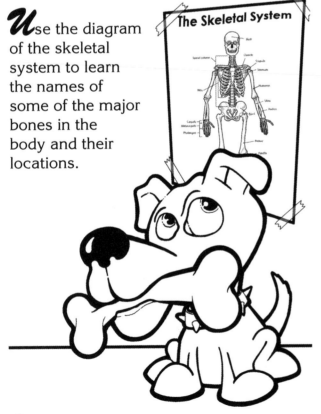

The Skeletal System

Dem BONES

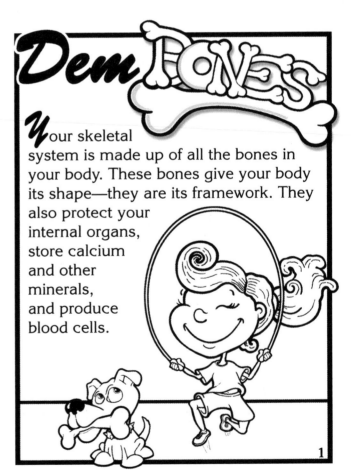

Your skeletal system is made up of all the bones in your body. These bones give your body its shape—they are its framework. They also protect your internal organs, store calcium and other minerals, and produce blood cells.

8

1

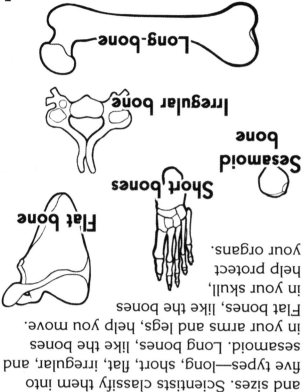

Your bones come in different shapes and sizes. Scientists classify them into five types—long, short, flat, irregular, and sesamoid. Long bones, like the bones in your arms and legs, help you move. Flat bones, like the bones in your skull, help protect your organs.

Long bone

Irregular bone

Sesamoid bone

Short bones

Flat bone

When you are born, you have about 300 bones. As you grow, some of these bones fuse together. By the time you are an adult and have stopped growing, you will only have 206 bones.

300 Bones

206 Bones

Your skeletal system is divided into two parts. One part is called the axial skeleton. The other part is called the appendicular skeleton. The axial skeleton is made up of the skull, the spine, the rib cage, and the sternum.

The Axial skeleton

Beneath the hard bone is spongy bone (also called cancellous bone). It is very strong, but not as hard as the cortical bone layer. In the very center of some bones is the bone marrow. This is where blood cells are made.

Spongy bone

Bone marrow

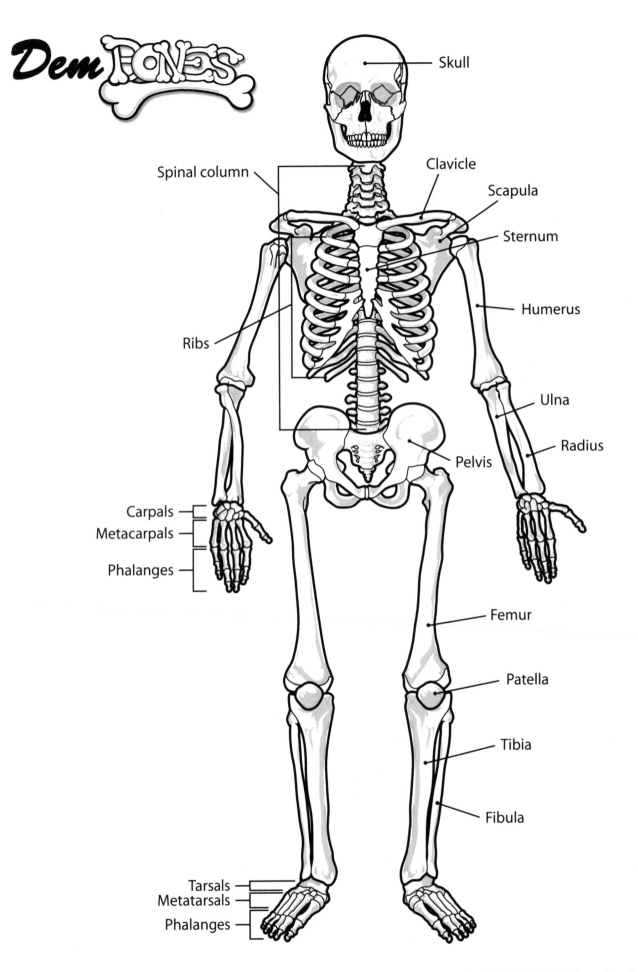

Dem Bones

Skull

Spinal column

Clavicle

Scapula

Sternum

Humerus

Ribs

Ulna

Radius

Pelvis

Carpals

Metacarpals

Phalanges

Femur

Patella

Tibia

Fibula

Tarsals

Metatarsals

Phalanges

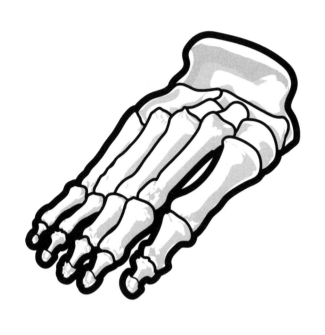

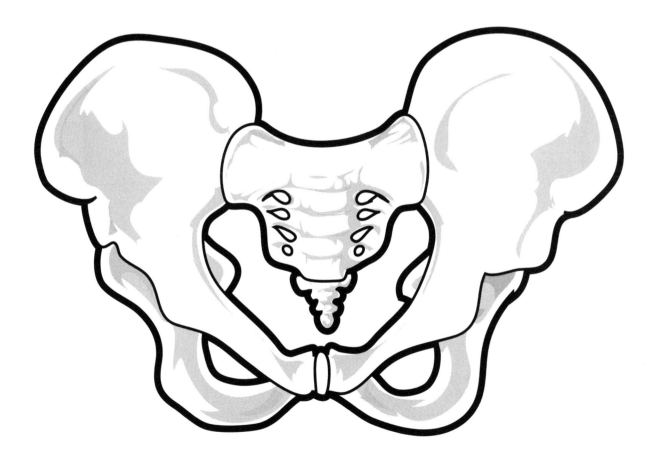

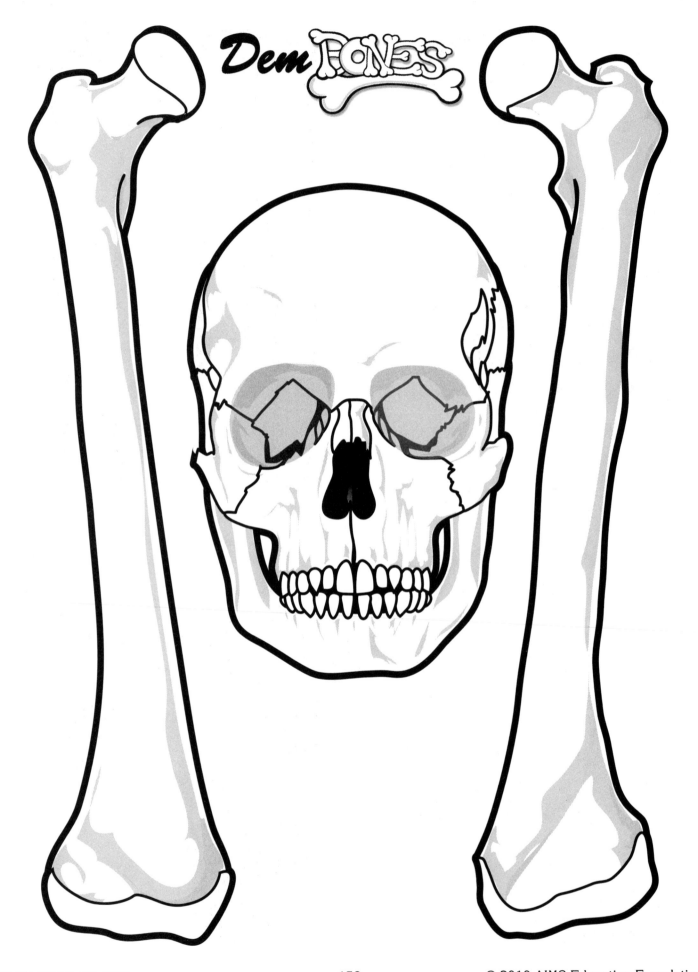

Dem BONES

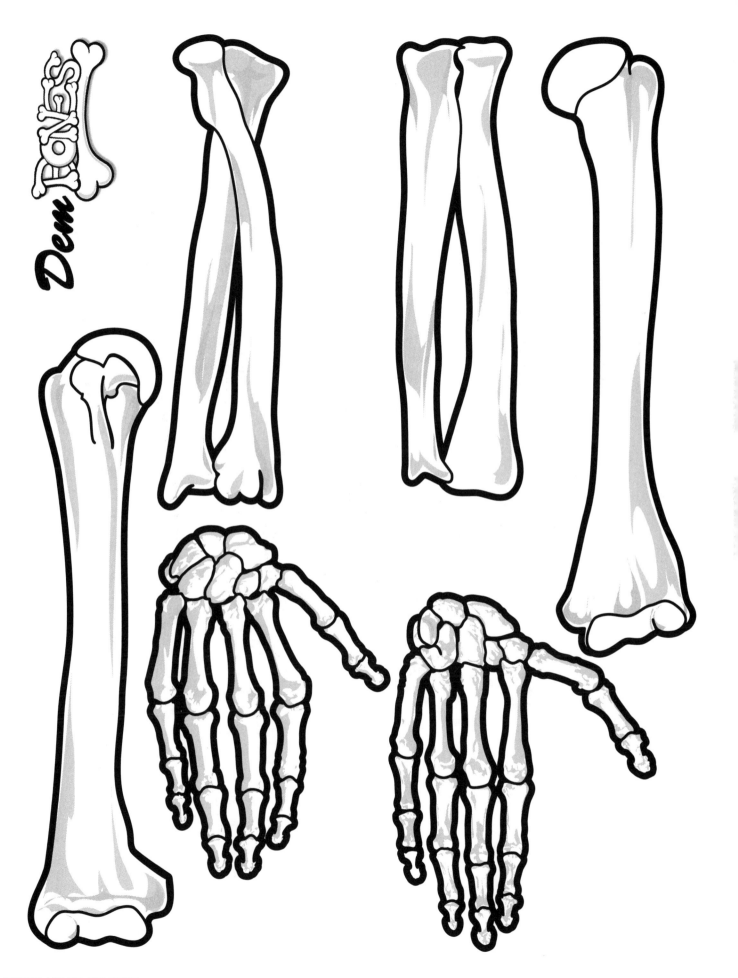

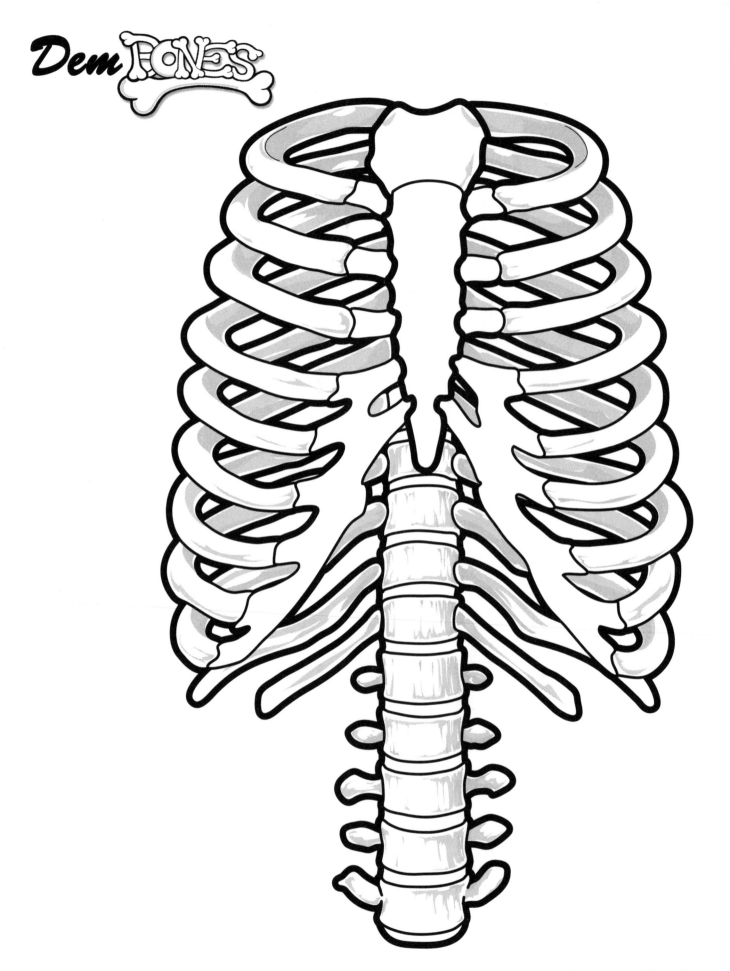

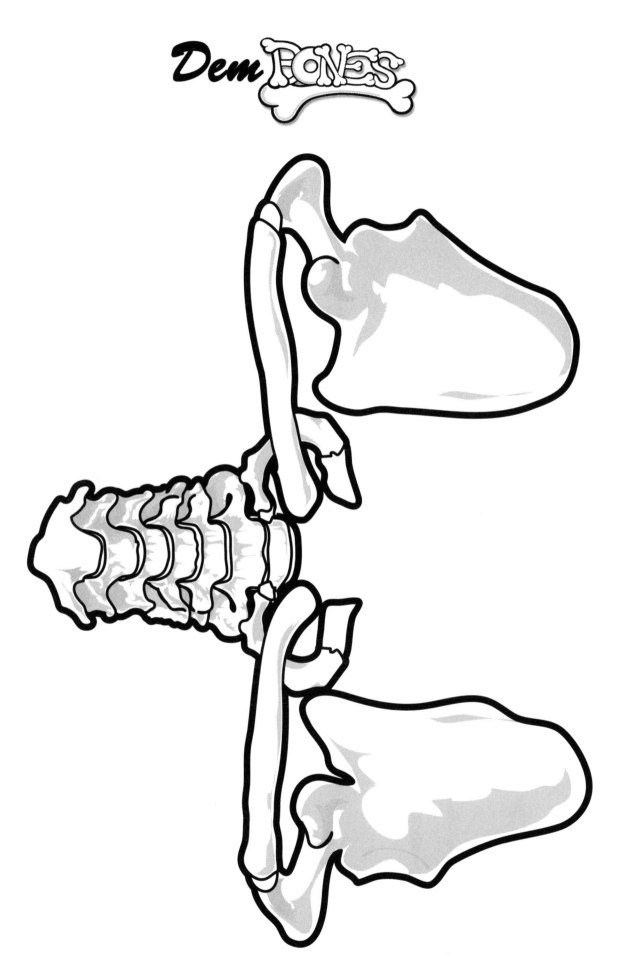

161

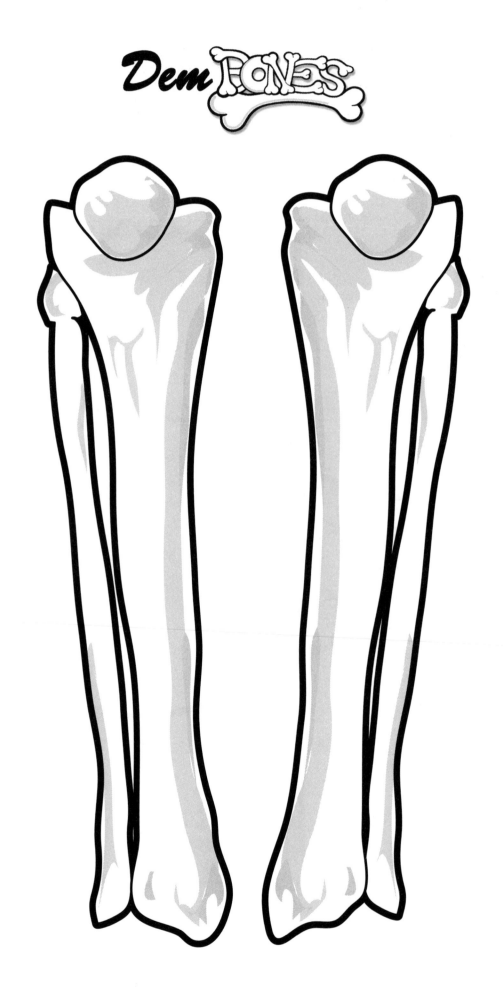

162

Connecting Learning

1. What is the purpose of the skeletal system?

2. How many bones would you guess are in your body right now? Justify your response.

3. Where is your femur? ...your radius? ...your pelvis? ...your clavicle? ...etc.

4. How does your skeleton model compare to an actual skeleton?

5. What are you wondering now?

Topic
Skeletal system

Key Questions
1. What is the inside of a leg bone like?
2. Why was the bone designed this way to complete its functions?

Learning Goals
Students will:
- recognize the general structures of bones and their functions, and
- become aware of the structural and functional purpose of bone physiology.

Guiding Document
NRC Standard
- *The human organism has systems for digestion, respiration, reproduction, circulation, excretion, movement, control, and coordination, and for protection from disease. These systems interact with one another.*

Science
Life science
    human body
        skeletal system

Integrated Processes
Observing
Comparing and contrasting
Generalizing
Applying

Materials
Beef bones (see *Management 1*)
Newspaper or butcher paper
Bleach water solution (see *Management 3*)
Soda cans (empty)
Scissors
Glue
Student pages

Background Information
The design of our bones is awesome. They provide the solid structure for our bodies while allowing flexibility for motion and stress. They can support a force of 24,000 pounds per square inch, yet provide a cushioned landing to each step we take. They do all this while manufacturing our bodies' blood cells and providing our bodies with a storage facility for nutrients and minerals.

Bones are living parts of our bodies. They grow, maintain and repair themselves, and interact with our other body systems. Bones are made of specialized cells and protein fibers. Living tissue makes up 30% of a bone. This tissue is imbedded in a flexible matrix of water, minerals, and carbohydrates. Water makes up 25% of the content of a bone. Minerals—mostly calcium and phosphate—make up 45% of a bone.

The long bones in the human body are roughly cylindrical in shape. The cylinder is one of the strongest shapes because it evenly distributes stress throughout its length. The outsides of bones are made up a very solid *hard bone* (cortical bone), where the crystal nature of the minerals provides strength. This strength is located on the outside of the bone where it provides the most leverage in keeping the bone rigid.

Inside the hard bone is a layer of *spongy bone* (cancellous bone) that has a lattice-type structure. The beams of the lattice form along the lines of greatest pressure, making bones both strong and light. When the marrow in the cavity of the bone is removed, struts or braces of spongy bone can be seen running along lines of stress. As the bone widens at each end, the area of spongy bone becomes larger. This increased area of spongy bone allows bones to act as shock absorbers.

Inside both the hard bone and the spongy bone is a cavity filled with a jelly-like or fatty material called *marrow*. The marrow is responsible for blood cell production. At birth, all bone marrow is involved in producing blood cells, and the marrow is red and filled with blood vessels. As an individual matures, the marrow in long bones gradually becomes yellow marrow and no longer produces blood cells, but is used for storage.

The design of a hard, dense outer shell, filled with a honeycomb material maximizes strength and minimizes weight. The added advantage is a very secure cavity for the essential production of blood cells.

The chemical matrix of bone construction allows for the quick addition and depletion of minerals. This attribute, along with the presence the circulatory system for blood cell production, makes bones a convenient place for mineral storage. If the body has excess minerals, they are stored in the bones and can be quickly withdrawn when the need arises.

The exterior of the bone allows it to interact within its system and with other systems of the body. A thin membrane called the *periosteum* covers the entire surface of the bone. It contains the blood vessels that supply the nutrients to the bone, and the nerves that signal pain.

On the ends of bones, where they form joints with other bones, is a very slippery and tough material called *cartilage*. The cartilage acts as grease in the joint, allowing the bones to flex smoothly with little friction.

Management
1. This activity requires beef bones from the legs that have been cut in half lengthwise. Find a local butcher who has several bones and ask that the bones be cut lengthwise on the band saw. If not enough bones are available, each bone half can be cut in two pieces containing one joint to the center of the length of the bone.
2. If only one bone is available, the two halves can be placed in a center where students have an opportunity to complete the record sheet. When the entire class has made observations and records, the generalizing and summarizing part of the activity can be completed.
3. The work area should be covered with butcher paper or newspaper. After the investigation, the area should be sanitized by washing it with a bleach water solution or another antiseptic.

Procedure
1. Have students discuss what they think the inside of a bone is like and why they think it is formed that way.
2. Distribute the bones and have students observe them in cross-sections, comparing and contrasting different areas of the bones.
3. With the bone present for observations, have the students make a record in one of two ways:
   a. The students cut out and glue the appropriate parts to the representative area of the bone outline on the student record page.
   b. The students draw an accurate picture of the bone showing the different areas they have identified. Students may turn the bone over on

their papers so the outside is facing up and trace the outline. The bone will leave grease, blood, and water marks to identify different areas.

4. Have students cut out the information cards and glue them to their student pages. They should then draw a line connecting each card to the area(s) it describes.

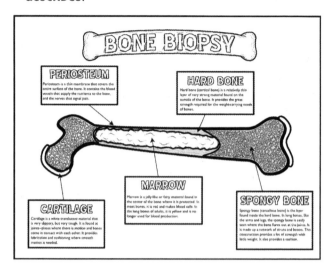

5. Lead a class discussion on how the bone was different from what they had anticipated. Discuss the design aspects that go into the different parts of the bone and how the form of each area is matched to a structural or functional need of the bone. See the *Background Information* for details.
6. Show an empty soda can to the class and ask them how the can is similar to and different from the bone.
7. Have a student carefully stand on the top of an empty soda can so it does not crush. While the student is standing on the can, tap the lateral surface of the can so that it collapses.
8. Discuss with students why the can did not collapse until it was tapped, and the similarity of the bone's design to the can's.

Connecting Learning
1. How are areas of the bone different from each other?
2. From its appearance, why is each area structured the way it is? [cartilage: smooth for sliding; spongy bone: absorb shock, storage in space; hard bone: strength; marrow: storage, blood cell production]
3. Why do you think the bone was designed with a space in the middle? [storage, weighs less than solid hard bone, protection of interior material, gives body bulk]
4. Compare and contrast a soda can and a bone. [both store something inside, both strong on outside and space inside, can is made of one material, bone is made of combination of materials]

5. A soda can's design allows it to hold up something many times its own weight. Why do you think a bone with a space in the center is important in its design? [strength with minimal material]
6. What are you wondering now?

Extension

Make a rubbery bone by placing the bone of a chicken drumstick in a cup of vinegar for several days to a week. Take it out and it should be very pliable like rubber. Let it dry out for a couple of days and the bone will become a flexible leather-like material. This demonstrates in reverse the process of bone calcification. At birth, most bones are cartilaginous in nature. This allows for flexibility at birth and during youth. As an individual ages, calcium replaces or impregnates the cartilage, turning it to bone. The acid in the vinegar reverses the process by removing the calcium and reducing the hard bone to a cartilaginous-like material.

Internet Connections

KidsHealth®
http://kidshealth.org/kid/htbw/
Select the bone from the scrolling list for information on the bones, diagrams, movies, and more.

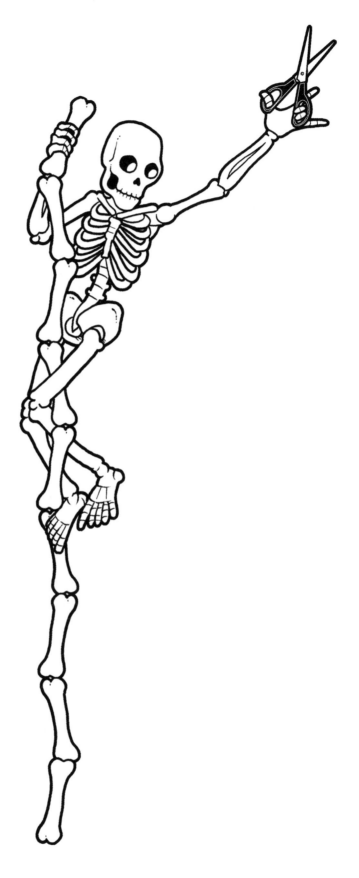

BONE BIOPSY

Key Questions

1. What is the inside of a leg bone like?

2. Why was the bone designed this way to complete its functions?

Learning Goals

Students will:

- recognize the general structures of bones and their functions, and

- become aware of the structural and functional purpose of bone physiology.

BONE BIOPSY

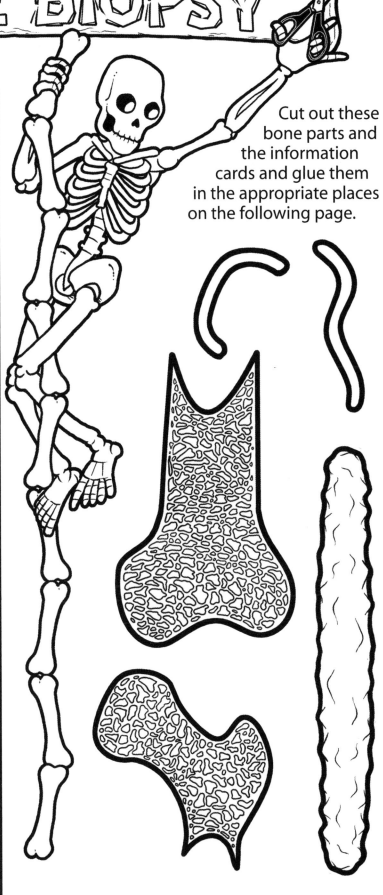

Cut out these bone parts and the information cards and glue them in the appropriate places on the following page.

CARTILAGE

Cartilage is a white translucent material that is very slippery, but very tough. It is found at joints—places where there is motion and bones come in contact with each other. It provides lubrication and cushioning where smooth motion is needed.

HARD BONE

Hard bone (cortical bone) is a relatively thin layer of very strong material found on the outside of the bone. It provides the great strength required for the weight-carrying needs of bones.

SPONGY BONE

Spongy bone (cancellous bone) is the layer found inside the hard bone. In long bones, like the arms and legs, the spongy bone is easily seen where the bone flares out at the joints. It is made up a network of struts and beams. This construction provides a lot of strength with little weight. It also provides a cushion.

MARROW

Marrow is a jelly-like or fatty material found in the center of the bone where it is protected. In most bones, it is red and makes blood cells. In the long bones of adults, it is yellow and is no longer used for blood production.

PERIOSTEUM

Periosteum is a thin membrane that covers the entire surface of the bone. It contains the blood vessels that supply the nutrients to the bone, and the nerves that signal pain.

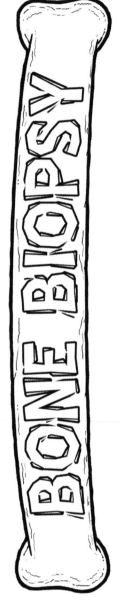

BONE BIOPSY

Draw or glue the parts of a bone in the appropriate places on the bone outline. Glue the information cards on the paper and draw a line from each card to the area(s) it describes.

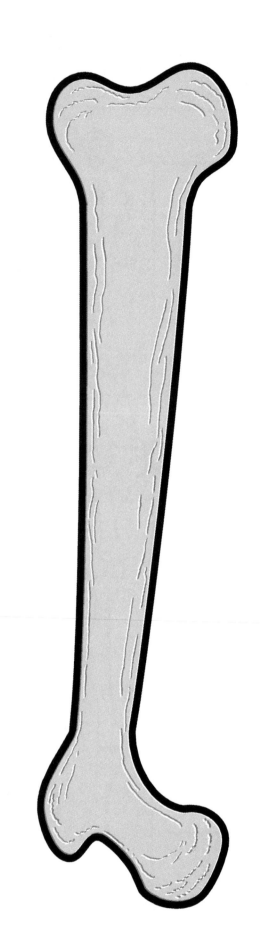

BONE BIOPSY

Connecting Learning

1. How are areas of the bone different from each other?

2. From its appearance, why is each area structured the way it is?

3. Why do you think the bone was designed with a space in the middle?

4. Compare and contrast a soda can and a bone.

5. A soda can's design allows it to hold up something many times its own weight. Why do you think a bone with a space in the center is important in its design?

6. What are you wondering now?

11

You can also do this with the muscles in your eyelids. Your eyes are constantly blinking to keep your eyes moist and to keep out dust and other particles. But you have the ability to blink or wink on command, to hold your eyes closed, or to hold one eye open at a time.

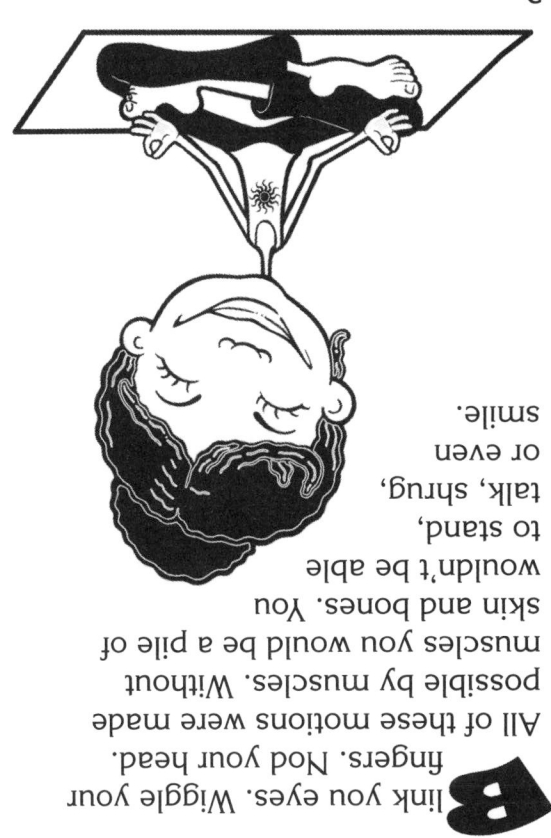

Blink you eyes. Wiggle your fingers. Nod your head. All of these motions were made possible by muscles. Without muscles you would be a pile of skin and bones. You wouldn't be able to stand, talk, shrug, or even smile.

The next time you lift a book or take a walk or eat an apple, think about all the muscles you have working together to make it possible.

Many Muscles

12

1

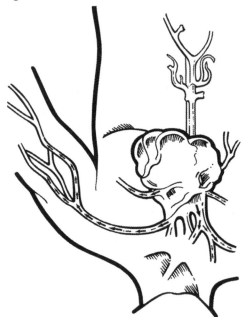

Cardiac muscle is a special kind of involuntary muscle. It's only found in the heart. Your heart muscle pumps about 100,000 times each day to move blood through your body.

You have about 600 skeletal muscles in your body. The largest is the *gluteus maximus*. This is the muscle on your bottom. The smallest muscle is inside your ear. It is called the *stapedius*. It is just a little over one millimeter long.

Gluteus maximus

Some of your muscles are normally controlled by your brain but can also be controlled by you if you think about it. You breathe all day and all night without giving it much thought, but if you want, you can hold your breath, take a deep breath, or breathe in and out very quickly.

You have three kinds of muscles in your body—skeletal, smooth, and cardiac. Skeletal muscles are what you usually think of when you think of muscles. These are the muscles that are attached to your bones. They help you walk, talk, lift, carry, squat, bend, smile, and more.

Cardiac

Skeletal

Smooth

10

3

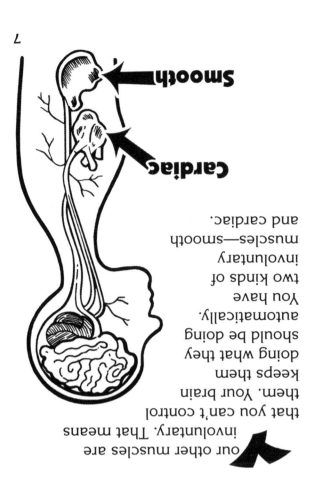

Smooth

Cardiac

our other muscles are involuntary. That means that you can't control them. Your brain keeps them doing what they should be doing automatically. You have two kinds of involuntary muscles—smooth and cardiac.

Triceps

biceps

uscles can only pull; they cannot push. That means that many skeletal muscles need to work in pairs to help your body parts move. Your arms are a good example. You have one muscle—the biceps—that pulls on your forearm, allowing you to bring your hand to your shoulder. Its pair—the triceps—pulls on the back of your elbow, making your arm straight again.

Smooth muscles are found in your digestive system. They contract and relax to move food through your body. The iris in your eye is also a smooth muscle. It controls the amount of light that comes into your eyes through the pupils. Your bladder is another place where smooth muscles are at work.

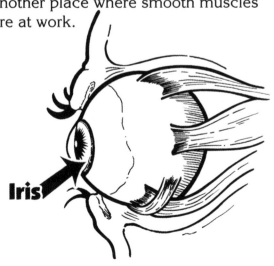

Iris

Skeletal muscles are also called voluntary muscles because these are the muscles that you can control. You can lift your arms, kick your legs, smile, frown, and pick up a pencil just by thinking about it and doing it.

FROM HEAD TO TOE

HANDS AND FINGERS, MUSCLES AND BONES

Topic
Musculoskeletal system

Key Question
How do muscles, tendons, and ligaments work together to move the finger?

Learning Goals
Students will:
- learn the functions of muscles, tendons, and ligaments;
- build a working model of a forefinger; and
- identify the parts of the model that correspond to the parts of a forefinger and their functions.

Guiding Documents
Project 2061 Benchmarks
- *Like other animals, human beings have body systems for obtaining and providing energy, defense, reproduction, and the coordination of body functions.*
- *Geometric figures, number sequences, graphs, diagrams, sketches, number lines, maps, and stories can be used to represent objects, events, and processes in the real world, although such representations can never be exact in every detail.*

NRC Standard
- *The human organism has systems for digestion, respiration, reproduction, circulation, excretion, movement, control, and coordination, and for protection from disease. These systems interact with one another.*

Science
Life science
    human body
        musculoskeletal system

Integrated Processes
Observing
Comparing and contrasting
Applying

Materials
Rulers
Scissors
Glue sticks
Paper clips
Transparent tape
Plastic drinking straws (see *Management 3*)
Crochet thread or kite string (see *Management 4*)
Rubber bands (see *Management 5*)
Student pages

Background Information
Cells are the basic building blocks of plants and animals. Groups of similar cells form different types of *tissues* that perform special functions, such as muscle tissue, bone tissue, heart tissue, and brain tissue.

In the human body, the skeletal system provides a strong and flexible framework on which to hang the fleshy parts of the body. Muscles attached to this flexible framework make it possible to move parts of the body or the whole body. Muscles exert forces on bones by converting chemical energy in the muscle tissue to shorten and relax the muscle. Muscles pull, but they cannot push.

Muscles are approximately two-fifths of body weight. Bands of a tough, fibrous material called *tendons* attach muscles to bones. *Ligaments* are tough and slightly elastic bands of tissue that connect bones to other bones.

In this activity, students learn about the major bone groups of the wrist and hand, the *carpals, metacarpals,* and *phalanges.* Students then construct a simple working model of the forefinger. From the model, students will learn the function of muscles, tendons, and ligaments.

Management
1. Gather the materials and construct a model to show your students what they will be building. Knowing the construction steps will also help you better assist your students to successfully construct a model.
2. Copy the *Finger Pattern* and *Finger Model* pages on card stock. Each pair of students will need one copy of each page.
3. Cut plastic drinking straws into 1 ½-inch lengths. Each group will need two straw lengths.
4. Cut crochet thread or kite string into 12-inch lengths. Each group will need two threads.

5. Cut rubber bands into 1 ½-inch lengths. The rubber bands should be thin (such as #19) or they will create too much resistance. Each group will need one piece of rubber band.

Procedure

1. Distribute the *Human Hand Fact Page* to students. Read through the information on the page and discuss any new vocabulary.

2. Have students get into pairs and distribute the *Finger Pattern* page, the instructions for constructing the phalanges and metacarpal bones, and the necessary materials to each pair.

3. Tell the students to follow the instructions to construct the phalanges and metacarpal bones.

4. When groups are ready, distribute the instructions for constructing the base along with the additional materials necessary.

5. After groups have completed their bases, distribute the final page of instructions and the remaining materials.

6. Have them work together to assemble the model finger.

7. Show students how to pull the strings to make the finger move up and down. This may take some practice to perfect. Depending on how tightly students attached their rubber band ligaments, the top tendon may or may not be needed to straighten the finger out.

8. Discuss the model and what it shows about the human forefinger and how it works.

Connecting Learning

1. What does pulling on one of the strings represent? [shortening, or contracting, the muscles]

2. How does the model illustrate that muscles can only pull and not push? [pushing on either string will not lower or raise the finger]

3. What is the purpose of tendons? [connect muscles to bones]

4. What part of the model represents the tendons? [the strings]

5. What do ligaments do? [connect bones]

6. Where on your model can you find a ligament? [the rubber band that connects the metacarpal piece to the phalange piece]

7. Why can't you bend your forefinger above the horizontal? [The shape of the phalange and metacarpal pieces keep the phalanges from moving up.]

8. How is your model like a real finger? [It shows the location of the bones, muscles, ligaments, and tendons; it shows how the finger moves; etc.] How is it unlike a real finger? [The muscles on the model do not contract; each phalange in my real forefinger can move; etc.]

9. Hold out your forefinger and, keeping the phalanges stiff, wag the finger up and down. Describe the instructions you gave to your finger that caused your whole forefinger to move up and down. (Students will find it difficult to identify a specific set of instructions given to the forefinger that causes it to stiffen and wag up and down. It's an example of the marvelous control humans have over the muscles and bones in the human body.)

10. Now wag your forefinger up and down, but this time, curl the finger. How does this action compare to wagging the stiffened forefinger? (Students will use words that describe the difference as "feeling" different.)

11. What are you wondering now?

Internet Connections

TeensHealth™

http://teenshealth.org/teen/your_body/body_basics/bones_muscles_joints.html

This article on the musculoskeletal system includes information on muscles and bones and how they work together as well as interactive diagrams.

HANDS AND FINGERS, MUSCLES AND BONES

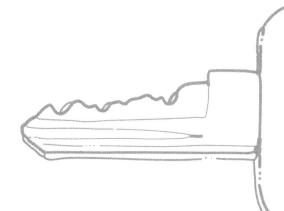

Key Question

How do muscles, tendons, and ligaments work together to move the finger?

Learning Goals

Students will:

- learn the functions of muscles, tendons, and ligaments;

- build a working model of a forefinger; and

- identify the parts of the model that correspond to the parts of a forefinger and their functions.

HANDS AND FINGERS, MUSCLES AND BONES

HUMAN HAND FACT PAGE

The structure of your body is given by your bones. There are over 200 bones in your body! Some are big, like your leg bones. Others are tiny, like the bones in your ear.

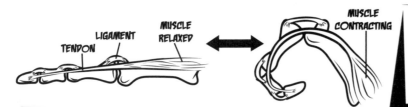

Connected to your bones are muscles. Muscles allow you to move your body parts by contracting (getting smaller). Muscles only pull. They cannot push.

Tendons hold your muscles to your bones. They are bands of tough, fibrous material. Ligaments connect bones to other bones. They are tough, elastic bands of tissue.

Your hands are an important part of your body. You use them every day to do all kinds of things. Your hands let you pick up your pencil. Your hands let you open and close doors.

Your hands are made of bones, muscles, tendons, and ligaments. They all work together to let you move your fingers and wrists.

There are eight bones in your wrist. They are called the *carpals*. The carpals connect to the *metacarpals*. These are the five bones that make up the palm of your hand.

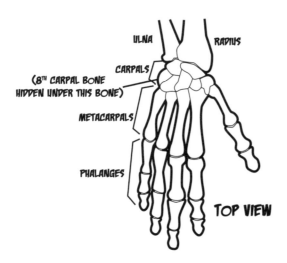

TOP VIEW

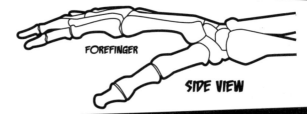

FOREFINGER

SIDE VIEW

The metacarpals connect to the *phalanges*. The phalanges are your finger bones. There are three phalanges in each finger and two in each thumb. All of these bones are connected with ligaments.

HANDS AND FINGERS, MUSCLES AND BONES

FINGER PATTERN

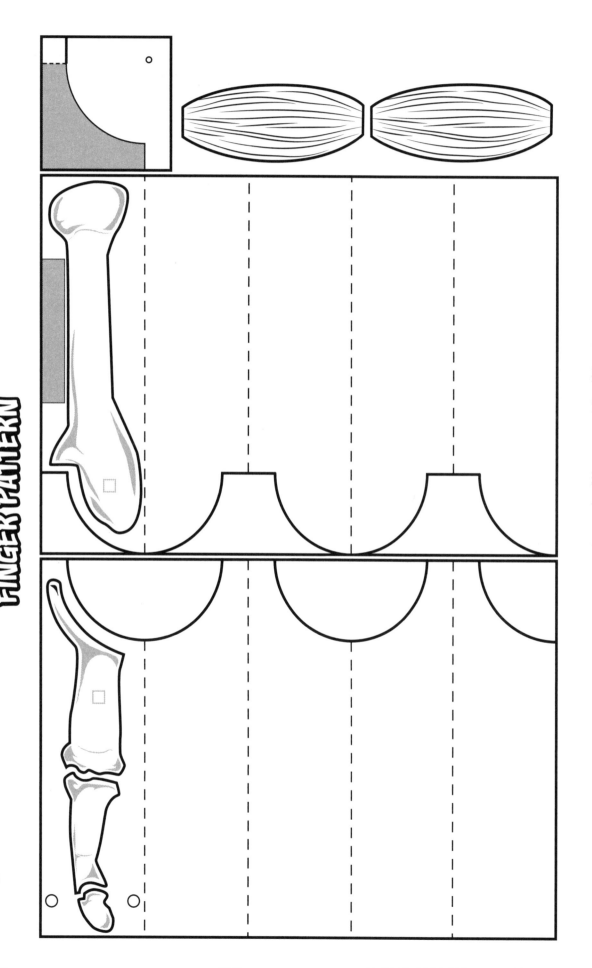

181

HANDS AND FINGERS, MUSCLES AND BONES

CONSTRUCTING THE PHALANGES AND METACARPAL BONES

MATERIALS

Glue stick	Scissors
Finger Pattern page	Ruler

1 Cut out the *Phalanges* pattern along the rectangular outline. Use a ruler to score along the dashed lines.

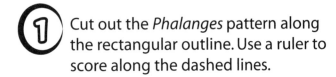

2 Fold the pattern so that the phalanges picture is on top. Glue the five layers of the pattern together to form a single piece.

3 Cut through all five layers along the solid curved line.

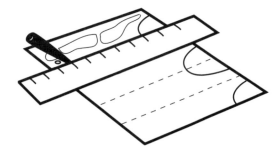

4 Repeat this process with the *metacarpal* pattern.

5 Cut out the square piece and carefully glue the phalanges piece to the square so that the curved end of the phalanges piece fits over the curved section of the square piece.

6 Cut along the solid line and fold up the small tab along the dashed line.

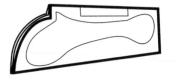

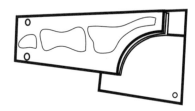

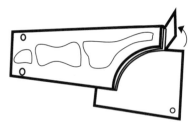

HANDS AND FINGERS, MUSCLES AND BONES
CONSTRUCTING THE BASE

MATERIALS
Glue stick   Paper clip
Scissors   *Finger Model* page

① Bend the paper clip as shown in the diagram. The smaller loop of the clip is bent up and then opened.

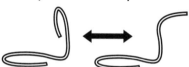

② Use the paper clip to punch a hole in the *Finger Model* page at the circle just below the front of the *metacarpal* piece. Cover the hole with a piece of transparent tape. (The tape will keep the hole from getting bigger when the completed model is operated.)

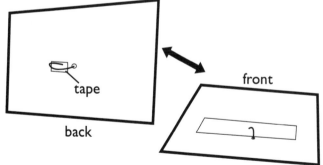

③ Use the paper clip to punch a hole in the circle on the square piece glued to the *phalanges* piece.

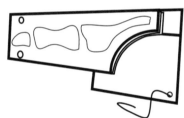

④ Turn the page over. Insert the spread end of the smaller loop of the paper clip into the hole. (This will break the tape covering the hole.) Tape the large loop to the bottom of the page.

⑤ Slide the phalanges piece over the paper clip.

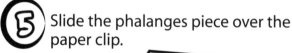

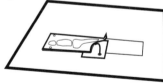

back   front   tape

⑥ Apply glue to the shaded area on the metacarpal pattern and set the metacarpal piece onto the pattern. Adjust the pieces so that the phalanges piece rotates freely under the rounded end of the metacarpal piece. The small folded up tab on the square piece should prevent the finger from rotating past straight.

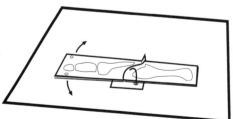

HANDS AND FINGERS, MUSCLES AND BONES

FINGER MODEL

What part of this model represents a tendon?

What is the function of a tendon?

What part of this model represents a muscle?

What is the function of a muscle?

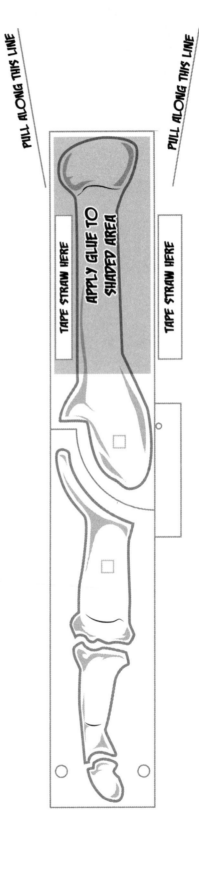

PULL ALONG THIS LINE

PULL ALONG THIS LINE

TAPE STRAW HERE

APPLY GLUE TO SHADED AREA

TAPE STRAW HERE

What is the function of a ligament?

What part of this model represents a ligament?

HANDS AND FINGERS, MUSCLES AND BONES

ATTACHING THE TENDONS AND LIGAMENTS

MATERIALS

Drinking straw pieces	Tape
Piece of rubber band	Crochet thread

1 Drop the thread through each straw piece and then tape the straws to the positions shown above and below the metacarpal bone.

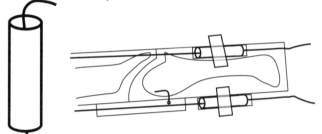

2 Cut out the muscles and tape them over the pieces of drinking straw.

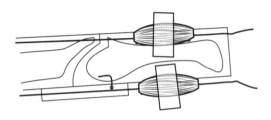

3 Tape the ends of the threads to the circles at the left end of the phalanges piece.

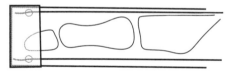

4 Tape the ends of the rubber band piece across the joint at the small squares printed on the phalanges and metacarpal pieces.

5 Pull the strings along the lines printed on the page to make the finger move up and down. Complete the page by identifying the parts of the model and their functions.

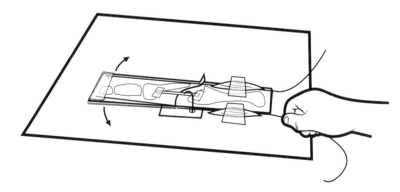

© 2010 AIMS Education Foundation

Connecting Learning

1. What does pulling on one of the strings represent?

2. How does the model illustrate that muscles can only pull and not push?

3. What is the purpose of tendons?

4. What part of the model represents the tendons?

5. What do ligaments do?

6. Where on your model can you find a ligament?

7. Why can't you bend your forefinger above the horizontal?

Connecting Learning

8. How is your model like a real finger? How is it unlike a real finger?

9. Hold out your forefinger and, keeping the phalanges stiff, wag the finger up and down. Describe the instructions you gave to your finger that caused your whole forefinger to move up and down.

10. Now wag your forefinger up and down, but this time, curl the finger. How does this action compare to wagging the stiffened forefinger?

11. What are you wondering now?

187

WINGING IT!

Topic
Musculoskeletal system

Key Questions
1. How are the muscles and skeleton held together?
2. How to do the muscles and bones work together to provide motion?

Learning Goals
Students will:
- learn how muscles work together with the skeleton to provide motion, and
- learn how the muscle and skeletal system are held together.

Guiding Documents
Project 2061 Benchmark
- *Like other animals, human beings have body systems for obtaining and providing energy, defense, reproduction, and the coordination of body functions.*

NRC Standard
- *The human organism has systems for digestion, respiration, reproduction, circulation, excretion, movement, control, and coordination, and for protection from disease. These systems interact with one another.*

Science
Life science
    human body
        musculoskeletal system

Integrated Processes
Observing
Comparing and contrasting
Recording
Inferring

Materials
Chicken wings
Styrofoam meat trays
Butcher paper or newspaper
Cutting instrument (scalpel, craft knife, kitchen knife, one-bladed razor blade, large straight pins)
Colored pencils
Plastic or latex gloves, optional

Background Information
A chicken wing is anatomically analogous to the human arm. Although the major bones, joints, and muscle groups differ in size, their basic shape, location, and motions are the same.

As students carefully cut and pull back the skin on the wing, it reveals the muscles and skin formation. On the underside of the skin they should be able to see a small underlying layer of fat and the thin connective tissue between the skin and muscles. As they hold the skin up against a back light, they will be able to see capillary networks in the skin.

With the skin peeled back, students should be able to identify distinct muscle groups and can match them to those in their arms. The biceps on the inside of the upper wing, or front of the arm, and the triceps along the back of the upper wing and arm are the easiest to identify. The students can feel the thin sheathing that connects but separates the bundles of muscles. As students flex the wing by pushing and pulling the tip of the wing while holding the shoulder, they will see the opposing muscles in opposite conditions. As the biceps contract, the triceps are stretched.

As students are asked to carefully look at the elbow and wrist they will observe the white tendons that attach the muscles to the bones. They are easily found on the outsides and back of the elbow and wrist joints.

Working the muscles near the tendons with their fingers or a blunt object, like the rounded point of a worn pencil, students can begin to separate the muscle groups from each other.

As the muscle groups are separated, students can begin to observe how the contraction of each muscle affects the motion of the wing. Pulling on the biceps pulls the lower wing up. The counter motion of pulling on the triceps extends the lower wing. Similar motion can be made to the wing tip by pulling on the muscle on the top of the lower arm and then pulling on the muscles on the sides of lower wing. As students pull on the muscles they will see the white iridescent tendons move. They will also be able to see the space formed in joints or connective tissue that keep the tendons in the correct positions while allowing them to move. Students will be making these interesting observations as they entertain themselves making the chicken wing punch and wave.

When students carefully cut away the bulk of the muscles (meat) just above each tendon, they will expose the joints. When the muscles have been separated from the elbow joint, students can observe its construction. As they grab the upper and lower wing bones and pull them apart with a firm tension, they will separate the joint slightly and will see the white taunt ligaments. Carefully cutting or snipping these ligaments will allow the joint to be easily separated. As students pull the joint apart they expose the smooth white cartilage on the inside of the joint. As they feel it, they will recognize how the cartilage provides smooth, low-friction motion, while the ligaments keep the joint in tight alignment. By scraping the cartilage and the bones with a blunt instrument, they will recognize why the joints are more susceptible to injury then the bones.

Management

1. Chicken wings are easily purchased at a grocery store. One wing per group of four students works well. Chicken legs can be substituted for wings. Chicken legs are not as anatomically similar to human legs as wings are to arms, and they are more expensive. However, the skin is pulled back more easily on legs, and if working with younger students, legs may provide a better experience.

2. Putting sharp instruments into the hands of children can be dangerous. Before beginning the activity make sure that students are aware of the dangers and are coached in ways to avoid injury. Stress that their cutting motions move the knives down into tables or cutting boards and not up into people. Some teachers have found success in having students separate the skin and muscle groups by having one student pull the skin away from the meat while a second student scrapes at the connective tissue with the point of a straight pin.

3. To reduce the risk of exposure to salmonella, the work area should be covered with butcher paper or newspaper. After the investigation, the area should be sanitized by washing with a bleach water solution or another antiseptic.

4. If the danger with knives is too great for the class, the teacher may choose to dissect chicken wings to different levels and then just allow students to move from station to station making observations.

5. It is best to allow enough time in one day to get the investigation done unless you have adequate refrigeration to preserve the raw meat.

6. Most students are willing to work with a chicken wing, as it is a very familiar object, although for most of them it is cooked before they touch it. Some students do not want to work with a raw chicken wing. The teacher may choose to provide disposable gloves for students to wear, although they often make it harder for the students to work with the chicken wing. **Make sure students wash their hands thoroughly with soap and hot water after doing the investigation.**

Procedure

1. Distribute a dissecting tray (styrofoam meat tray) to each group with a chicken wing and the student pages. Have the students record the external differences and similarities between their arms and the chicken wing.

2. Have students identify and record the analogous parts of the wing and arm and color their locations the same.

3. After clearly discussing safety rules and practices, distribute the cutting instruments and gloves (optional). Have students cut and pull back the skin from the shoulder to the lower wing.

4. Instruct students to observe the interior of the skin and identify and record the underlayer of fat, connective tissue, and capillaries.

5. While pulling and pushing on the shoulder and wingtip, have students observe how muscles contract and extend and identify and label by color the chicken's biceps and triceps.

6. By carefully working the upper wing muscles with a finger or blunt instrument, have the students separate the muscles into groups of biceps and triceps. When the muscles are separated they can grasp each and alternately pull (contract) on each to make the lower wing punch. (Students may choose to follow a similar procedure on the lower wing to make it wave.)

7. As students make the wing punch by contracting opposing muscles, have them observe how the muscles connect to the bone. They should be able to identify and label by color the tendons as each moves through openings in the muscles or indentations around the joints.

8. After identifying the tendons, have the students cut them from the muscles around the elbow. As they remove the muscles, the elbow will be exposed.

9. As the students pull with a steady tension on the exposed elbow, a gap should open allowing them to see the taunt ligaments that hold the elbow together. After they identify the ligaments, have students cut them to separate the joint.

10. Have students touch the cartilage, and scrape it and the bone with a blunt object to observe the differences in texture and strength. Students should also notice where the ligaments and tendons attach to the bones, recording all their observations and labeling with color.

11. After cleaning up the investigation, have students summarize what they have learned about the muscles and skeletal systems and how they could apply that knowledge to themselves.

Connecting Learning

1. Externally, how are a chicken wing and your arm similar and different?
2. Why do you need two opposing muscles for every movement of your skeleton? [contract and extend, pull back and pull forth, muscles can't push]
3. Why does each end of a muscle need to attach to a different bone? [Muscles move a bone around a joint. If both ends of one muscle were attached to the same bone, it could only squish the bone.]
4. How are tendons and ligaments different? [tendons hold muscles to bones, and ligaments hold bones to bones]
5. Why are joints more likely to be injured than bones?
6. What are you wondering now?

Internet Connections

TeensHealth™
http://teenshealth.org/teen/your_body/body_basics/bones_muscles_joints.html
This article on the musculoskeletal system includes information on muscles and bones and how they work together as well as interactive diagrams.

Key Questions

1. How are the muscles and skeleton held together?

2. How to do the muscles and bones work together to provide motion?

Learning Goals

Students will:

- learn how muscles work together with the skeleton to provide motion, and

- learn how the muscle and skeletal system are held together.

WINGING IT!

How is your arm like a chicken wing?

Compare and contrast wings and arms.

SHOULDER

UPPER ARM
DRUMSTICK

ELBOW

FOREARM
LOWER WING

WRIST

HAND
WING TIP

WINGING IT!

1. Carefully cut a slit down the wing from the shoulder to the lower wing. Try to cut from the inside of the skin to the outside so you do not cut up the muscles. Pull on the skin by the shoulder and pull it back to the lower wing. You might have to cut some of the connective tissue to help the skin separate. Identify the underlayer of fat, the capillaries, and connective tissue by coloring the label and part the same color.

2. Grab the wing by the wing tip and shoulder and pull and push it. Watch the muscles, and identify when muscles are stretched and squished. Identify the biceps and triceps by coloring the label and muscle the same color.

3. Carefully work your fingertip or a worn pencil tip between the muscles until they separate into the muscle groups. Pull on each group to see how the muscle makes the wing move. Notice how and where the muscle attaches to the bone. Use several muscle groups and see if you can get the wing to punch or wave. Identify the tendons and bones by coloring the label and the part the same color.

KEY

- ☐ UNDERLAYER FAT
- ☐ CAPILLARIES
- ☐ CONNECTIVE TISSUE
- ☐ BICEP
- ☐ TRICEP
- ☐ TENDONS
- ☐ BONES

WINGING IT!

Cut all the tendons around the elbow and pull away the muscles. Pull slowly on the bones to make a small gap in the elbow. You should be able to see the ligaments inside the joint. Cut the ligaments to separate the joint. Look and see how and where the ligaments and tendons attach. Feel the cartilage in the joint where the bones touch. Scrap the cartilage and bone to see how different they are. Identify all the labeled parts by coloring them the same color.

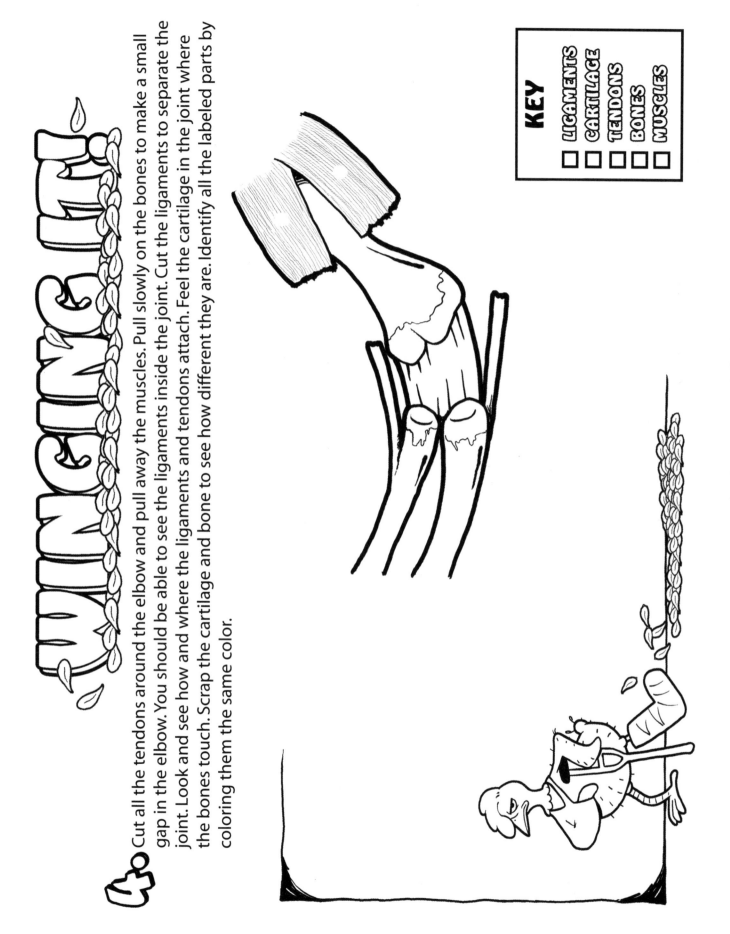

KEY

- ☐ LIGAMENTS
- ☐ CARTILAGE
- ☐ TENDONS
- ☐ BONES
- ☐ MUSCLES

Connecting Learning

1. Externally, how are a chicken wing and your arm similar and different?

2. Why do you need two opposing muscles for every movement of your skeleton?

3. Why does each end of a muscle need to attach to a different bone?

4. How are tendons and ligaments different?

5. Why are joints more likely to be injured than bones?

6. What are you wondering now?

Isn't It Interesting...
Musclebound

The hair on your arms stands up when you're frightened or cold because of some muscles located below the surface of your skin. When these muscles, the erector pili muscles, contract, up goes your hair!

Laugh away; it's good for the muscles. Scientists have found that laughter increases your heartbeat, thus supplying your body with a greater flow of oxygen-rich blood.

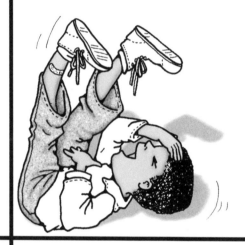

How's your sternocleidomastoic muscle? This is the longest one-word muscle name. You have two of these muscles. They are located in your neck and connect a bone behind your ear to your clavicle and your sternum. They help you tilt your head up and down and sideways.

Skeletal muscles make up about half of your weight. They help hold your skeleton in place and help you to move.

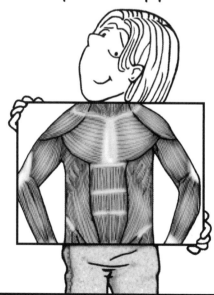

Have you ever brushed past a bush that was prickly or poked yourself on something sharp? Do you remember what happened? As soon as your nerve endings felt the sharp object, they sent a message that said, "Move! That's sharp!" Before you even had time to think about it, your hand or arm moved away from whatever was poking you. This is called a reflex action.

All of these things have to do with our sense of touch. We often associate our hands with the sense of touch, but they aren't the only places we can feel things. Run the eraser end of your pencil down your arm. What do you feel? Rub your shoe on the inside of your leg. What do you feel?

Our skin is very important. It protects our bodies from bacteria and viruses. It keeps our insides from drying out. It protects us from the sun's ultraviolet rays. It regulates our temperature, and it gives us information about our world.

Touchy Feely

How do you find a pencil in the bottom of your school bag without looking? Why does it hurt to walk on hot pavement? How can you tell the difference between cotton and silk?

Under the epidermis is the dermis. The dermis has blood vessels, oil glands, and sweat glands. It is also the layer where nerve endings can be found. In just one square inch of skin you can have over 1000 nerve endings!

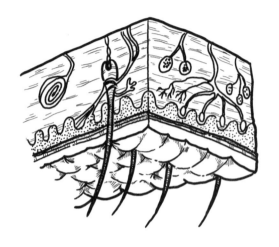

Your skin is made up of layers. The top layer is called the epidermis. New skin cells are made at the base of this layer. The top of the layer has dead skin cells. It is also where your body makes melanin. Melanin is what gives skin its color.

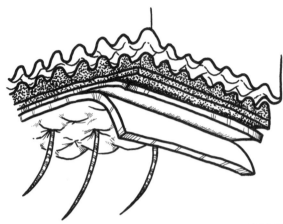

There are different kinds of nerve endings in your skin. They respond to different things like pain, heat, cold, and pressure/touch. These nerve endings send signals to your brain about the things that you feel. The brain interprets the signals so you know if something is sharp or smooth or cold or hot.

You can feel things pretty much anywhere on your body that's covered in skin. Your skin is one of your sensory organs. It is also the largest organ in your body. An average adult has about 1.8 square meters (19.4 square feet) of skin.

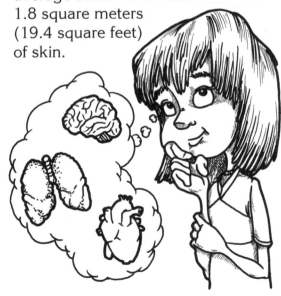

Topic
Skin

Key Question
What is the structure of our skin?

Learning Goals
Students will:
- make a model of the skin,
- label the parts, and
- describe their functions.

Guiding Documents
Project 2061 Benchmarks
- *Like other animals, human beings have body systems for obtaining and providing energy, defense, reproduction, and the coordination of body functions.*
- *Skin protects the body from harmful substances and other organisms and from drying out.*

NRC Standard
- *The human organism has systems for digestion, respiration, reproduction, circulation, excretion, movement, control, and coordination, and for protection from disease. These systems interact with one another.*

Science
Life science
  human body
    skin

Integrated Processes
Observing
Comparing and contrasting
Recording
Communicating

Materials
Craft foam, 3 colors (see *Management 1*)
Crochet thread, 5 colors (see *Management 2*)
Cord, 2 colors (see *Management 3*)
Yarn (see *Management 4*)
White glue
Ballpoint pen
Tape
Toothpicks
Scissors
Student pages

Background Information
Our skin is the largest organ in our body. Skin can be thin like the eyelids, or it can be thick like the skin on the soles of our feet. Skin can be hairy like our heads, or smooth like our lips. No matter the differences in our skin, it protects us from things such as bacteria, harsh chemicals, and the sun's ultraviolet rays, and it keeps us from drying out. The skin informs us about our world via sensory receptors that respond to things such as pain, pressure, touch, and temperature. Receptors (nerve endings) send impulses along the sensory nerves to the brain. Our skin also helps us with climate control. It contains sweat glands that release perspiration through our pores to help cool us when we're hot. The skin contains blood vessels that also help us control our body temperatures. When we get too hot, the blood circulation is stepped up. Blood vessels near the surface dilate, carrying some of our internal heat to the surface where it is lost to the air. One of our skin's responses to cold is goose bumps. Goose bumps are caused by the contraction of tiny muscles (erector pili) at the bottom of each hair. They cause our body hairs to fluff up, forming an insulating layer of air that helps keep us warm. (Porcupines have goose bumps that raise their quills.)

There are three major layers of skin:
- The top layer is the *epidermis*. This is the layer you can see. The base of the epidermis is where new skin cells are made. The top of the epidermis contains dead skin cells that slough off. The epidermis also makes melanin. Melanin gives the skin its color. Melanin helps protect the body from the sun's ultraviolet rays.
- The middle layer is the *dermis*. It contains blood vessels, oil and sweat glands, nerve receptors, and hair follicles. Blood vessels deliver oxygen and nutrients to the cells. They also take away carbon dioxide and other wastes. Oil glands (sebaceous glands) lubricate our skin and help it to be waterproof. The oil (sebum) also coats our hair, making it shiny. Sweat glands aid our bodies in maintaining an adequate body temperature. (When sweat is evaporated, our bodies are cooled.)
- The bottom layer of the skin is the *hypodermis* or *subcutaneous layer*. It is made up mostly of fat. The fat helps keep us warm. It also helps cushion bumps to our bodies. The hair follicles are rooted in the subcutaneous layer.

Management

1. Craft foam can be purchased in craft departments. Craft foam comes in different sizes. You will need three light colors. Usually one sheet each of two colors (the epidermis and hypodermis layers) will be enough for the class. Quantities for the third sheet (the dermis) depend on the size sheet you buy and the number of students you have. Each student will need the following:
   - Color One: one 1.5 cm x 8 cm piece (the epidermis layer)
   - Color Two: one 6.5 cm x 8 cm piece (the dermis layer)
   - Color Three: one 1.5 cm x 8 cm piece (the hypodermis/subcutaneous layer)

   It is easy to use a pencil or ballpoint pen for marking the foam. It should be cut with a paper cutter or scissors prior to doing the activity.

2. Crochet thread can be purchased in craft departments. It comes in a variety of colors. Choose bright colors that will show up on the craft foam you are using. Each student will need about 30 cm (1 foot) of each color. (You will have plenty of crochet thread left over to use for other projects during the school year.) To make a nerve model, students can wrap together three or four strands of crochet thread, attach it to the craft foam with a bead of glue, and separate the top ends to look like nerve endings.

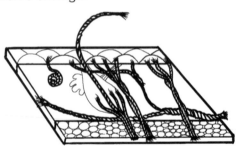

3. Multi-ply cord works well to represent blood vessels. Veins and arteries can be represented using the entire piece of cord. To represent the smaller capillaries, the plies can be separated to use just one ply.

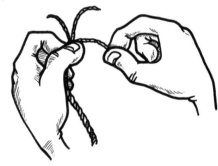

4. Yarn is used to represent hair.

Procedure

1. Ask the *Key Question* and state the *Learning Goals*.
2. Invite the students to share what they know about the skin.
3. Hand out the study print of the skin. Make certain that the students attend to the details of it (see *Background Information*):
   - the layers (the prefix *epi* in this case means *outer,* the prefix *hypo* means *under;* dermis comes from *derma* which is Latin for *skin);*
   - the nerve receptors of pain, touch, pressure, and temperature;
   - the blood vessels (arteries carry blood coming from the heart, veins carry blood going back to the heart);
   - the hair, sebaceous gland, and tiny muscle that causes goose bumps; and
   - the sweat gland.
4. Inform students that they are going to use this study print to fashion a model of the skin.
5. Distribute a *Sketch Pad* to each student. Show them the materials they will be using to make their models. Allow time for them to make their sketches, encouraging them to put the parts in the proper layer of the skin.
6. When sketches are completed, have students gather the materials they need for making their models. Distribute the next student page. Have students follow the directions to make their models. Direct them to glue a sample of the material used in the model on the key. If no material is used, have them make a sketch of the part on the key.
7. Distribute the parts and functions page. Tell students to match the part with its function.
8. Conclude with a discussion about the skin.

Connecting Learning

1. What is skin? [the largest organ in our body]
2. What is the function of skin? [It protects us, it helps keep our bodies at the right temperature, it keeps us from drying out, and it is full of sense receptors that inform us about our world.]
3. What are the layers of the skin? [epidermis, dermis, hypodermis (subcutaneous layer)]
4. Describe each layer.
5. How did the model help you better understand human skin?
6. What aspect of the skin most interested you?
7. How can our skin be harmed?

8. Besides being extremely painful, what are the harmful effects of being severely burned? [The skin protects our bodies from infections, etc. Severe burns open the body to infections and diseases. A severe burn also allows a body to lose valuable moisture, thus becoming dehydrated.]

9. What are you wondering now?

Extensions

1. Discuss why tattoo ink is injected into the dermis. [The cells in the epidermis slough off so a tattoo would not be permanent if it were injected in the top layer. This also helps to explain why tattoos are so difficult to remove.] Also note the fact that the danger of infections/diseases due to the use of dirty tattooing needles is great because the dermis is full of vessels that serve as a blood transport system to other parts of the body.

2. Topics of pimples can be discussed as students understand the role of the sebaceous glands in making sebum (oil) and the need to keep pores clean. The skin produces extra sebum during the adolescent years. The extra sebum can block the hair pores, allowing dirt, oil, and bacteria to collect underneath; hence, the red bump.

3. Investigate the problems of overexposure to ultraviolet rays.

Internet Connections

KidsHealth®
http://kidshealth.org/kid/htbw/skin.html
Select the skin from the scrolling list for information on the skin and its layers.

Solutions

Parts	Functions
Epidermis	The top layer of skin
Sensory Receptor	These sense pain, temperature, pressure, touch
Sebaceous Gland	This secretes sebum that lubricates the skin and hair
Dermis	The middle layer of skin
Arteries	These carry blood away from the heart to our body parts
Sweat Gland	This helps to cool our bodies when its product is evaporated
Veins	These carry blood from our body parts back to the heart
Hypodermis (Subcutaneous Layer)	The bottom layer of skin
Hair Follicle	The area from which hair grows

Key Question

What is the structure of our skin?

Learning Goals

Students will:

- make a model of the skin,
- label the parts, and
- describe their functions.

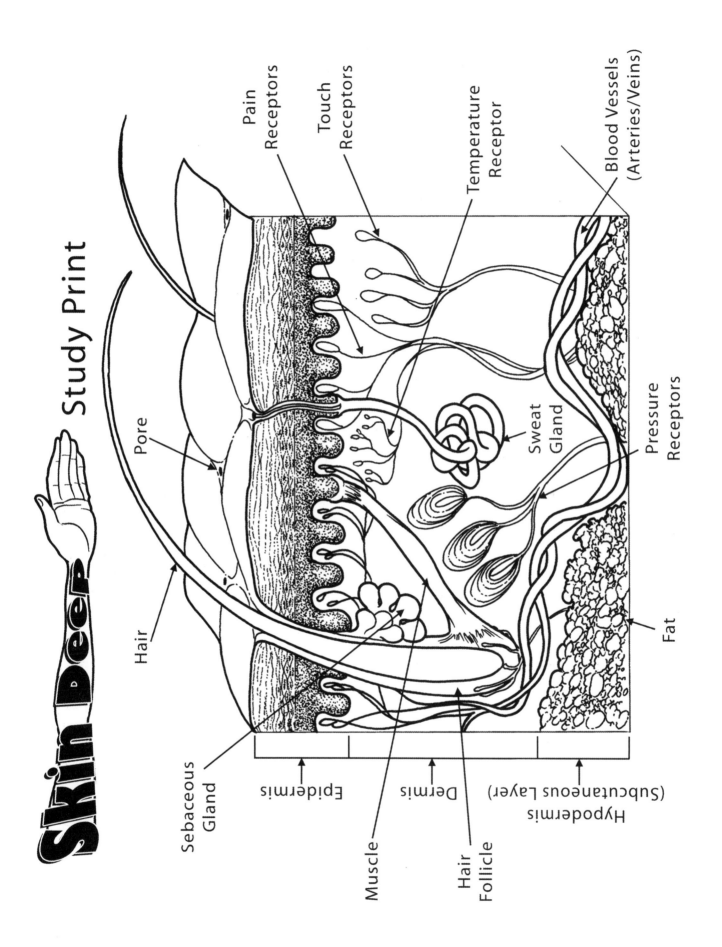

Study Print

Skin Deep

Pain Receptors

Touch Receptors

Temperature Receptor

Blood Vessels (Arteries/Veins)

Pore

Hair

Sebaceous Gland

Sweat Gland

Pressure Receptors

Fat

Epidermis

Dermis

Hypodermis (Subcutaneous Layer)

Muscle

Hair Follicle

Sketch Pads

epidermis

dermis

subcutaneous layer

epidermis

dermis

subcutaneous layer

epidermis

dermis

subcutaneous layer

epidermis

dermis

subcutaneous layer

Skin Deep

To make your model:

1. Tape the three pieces of craft foam together, placing the larger piece in the middle.
2. Use your pen to draw the pores, hair follicles, muscles, fat, and sebaceous gland on the surface of the craft foam.
3. The two colors of cording represent arteries and veins. Use white glue to attach them to the craft foam.
4. The crochet thread represents sensory receptors (nerves) and the sweat gland. Attach them to the craft foam using white glue.
5. Use yarn for hair, attaching it to the craft foam with white glue.
6. Tape your completed model to the page.
7. List the layers. Make a key to identify the parts of the skin.

Layers

1.
2.
3.

Tape your model here.

Key

Arteries

Veins

Pain Receptors

Touch Receptors

Pressure Receptors

Temperature Receptors

Sweat Gland

Hair

Hair Follicle

Muscle

Sebaceous Gland

Pore

Cut out the *Parts* and glue them to the appropriate function.

Parts

Dermis
Sebaceous Gland
Sweat Gland
Arteries
Hypodermis (Subcutaneous Layer)
Veins
Hair Follicle
Epidermis
Sensory Receptor

Functions

	The top layer of skin
	These sense pain, temperature, pressure, touch
	This secretes sebum that lubricates the skin and hair
	The middle layer of skin
	These carry blood away from the heart to our body parts
	This helps to cool our bodies when its product is evaporated
	These carry blood from our body parts back to the heart
	The bottom layer of skin
	The area from which hair grows

Connecting Learning

1. What is skin?

2. What is the function of skin?

3. What are the layers of the skin?

4. Describe each layer.

5. How did the model help you better understand human skin?

6. What aspect of the skin most interested you?

7. How can our skin be harmed?

8. Besides being extremely painful, what are the harmful effects of being severely burned?

9. What are you wondering now?

Topic
Sense of touch

Key Question
Which of the five places tested on your body is the most sensitive to touch?

Learning Goal
Students will perform a two-point discrimination test on five areas of their bodies to see how sensitive different locations are to touch.

Guiding Documents
NRC Standard
- *Use appropriate tools and techniques to gather, analyze, and interpret data.*

NCTM Standards 2000*
- *Collect data using observations, surveys, and experiments*
- *Represent data using tables and graphs such as line plots, bar graphs, and line graphs*

Math
Data analysis
   graphing
   measures of central tendency
     mode

Science
Life science
   human body
     senses

Integrated Processes
Observing
Comparing and contrasting
Collecting and recording data
Interpreting

Materials
For each group:
  16 paper clips
  8 index cards, 3" x 5"
  metric rulers
  pushpin
  tape
  construction instruction page
  role description page

For each student:
  sticky notes in two colors
  recording page
  graph page

Background Information
Receptors in our skin are sensitive to different stimuli from our environment. We have pain receptors, those that detect temperature (hot and cold), and those that detect various kinds of touch and/or pressure (vibration, movement, etc.). These receptors are not distributed evenly throughout our skin. Certain parts of our body have more of one kind or another. For example, the sides of the tongue have high concentrations of pain receptors. This is why it hurts so much when you bite your tongue. The parts of our body that are the most sensitive to touch are the tips of the fingers, the lips, the cheeks, the nose, and the palms of the hands. Some of the least sensitive areas are the legs, the shoulders, the back, and the arms.

One way to check for sensitivity to touch is to perform a two-point discrimination test (also called two-point gap discrimination test). This test is used by neurologists to check for certain disorders. In this test, a tool with two points (like the ends of a paper clip) is touched to the skin in the location being tested. The distance between the two points is gradually reduced until only one point is detectable. In areas that are more sensitive to touch, the threshold distance at which two points can be distinguished will be much smaller than in areas less sensitive to touch. A threshold of 6 mm or less is considered normal for the tips of the fingers.

Management
1. Be sensitive to any students who might have conditions that would cause their data to be significantly different from those of their classmates.
2. Students should work together in groups of four. Each student can be responsible for constructing two of the touch testers.
3. Make one or two touch testers ahead of time so students have reference samples when they are making their own.
4. Make an enlarged copy of the graph on the board or chart paper to use when graphing the class data.

5. A day or two prior to doing this activity, tell students that they will be testing the soles of their feet, their calves, and their forearms, so they will need to wear clothing that allows this.
6. Metric rulers (item number 1909) are available from AIMS.

Procedure

1. Write the following body parts down the board and separate them by horizontal lines: fingertip, cheek, forearm, calf, foot. Ask students which of these body parts they think would be most sensitive to touch.
2. Give each student a sticky note of the same color. Instruct students to label the notes with their names and to come and place the notes on the board next to the body part that they think will be the most sensitive to touch.
3. Explain that students will be working together in groups to perform an experiment that will test how sensitive different parts of the body are to touch.
4. Distribute the materials for the touch testers and the page of construction instructions to each group. Read through the instructions as a class and show students the sample tester you made so that everyone is clear on the process.
5. Allow time for groups to construct all eight of their touch testers.
6. Give each group the page that describes the roles of tester, subject, and recorder. Go through each responsibility and model the procedure with a student volunteer at the front of the class with you acting as the tester. Emphasize the importance of the subject not looking at what the tester is doing and the tester being consistent in how and where the touch is applied. Be sure students understand that they can begin with any of the testers; the response of the subject will tell them whether they need to continue testing with narrower or wider testers. Also emphasize that subjects should be completely honest about what they are able to feel; remind students that this is not a competition—without honest answers, the data will be meaningless.
7. Distribute a recording page to each student. Instruct them to record their names on the line that says "Subject." Explain that their data will be recorded on this page by one of the other members of their group for each location tested.
8. Instruct groups to begin testing. Have students test every student in the group in the same place (cheek, finger, arm, etc.) before moving on to the next body part. This will ensure that all students are continually participating in some part of the process.

9. When all of the data have been collected, distribute the graph page to each student. Have them graph their threshold values for each location. (These values should have been circled on their recording pages.)
10. Give students a sticky note of a different color and again have them record their names on the notes. Instruct them to put the second note on the board next to the name of the body part that was actually most sensitive to touch in their experiments.
11. Compare the results of different students and groups. Have groups share their mode threshold values for each of the body locations. Record these on the board and determine the mode threshold value for the class for each of the body locations.
12. Make a class graph with the mode threshold value for each of the locations. Discuss how this compares to individual students' results and the potential reasons for any differences.
13. Encourage students to explore the sensitivity of other body parts and learn more about the different sensory receptors in our skin.

Connecting Learning

1. Which of the body parts that we tested did you predict would be most sensitive to touch? Why did you think this?
2. How did the results compare to what you expected? Did everyone have the same results?
3. According to our class graph, which of the body parts we tested is the most sensitive to touch? …least sensitive?
4. Are there any locations that have about the same sensitivity to touch? How could we find out which is actually more sensitive? [Use more precise testers that go in increments smaller than half a centimeter.]
5. Did anyone's individual results vary from the most common results in the class? What might be some reasons for any differences? [differences in testing techniques, nerve damage, etc.]
6. Do you think that you can learn to be more touch sensitive in certain locations? Explain. [Studies have shown that repeated stimulation can enhance two-point discrimination, at least in the fingertips. For example, people who read in Braille have better than average tactile discrimination on their fingertips.]
7. What are you wondering now?

Extensions

1. Repeat the experiment on other parts of the body. Compare your results to the averages for these locations from clinical experiments.

Location	Threshold distance
Fingers	2-3mm
Upper Lip	5 mm
Cheek	6 mm
Nose	7 mm
Palm	10 mm
Forehead	15 mm
Foot	20 mm
Belly	30 mm
Forearm	35 mm
Upper arm	39 mm
Back	39 mm
Shoulder	41 mm
Thigh	42 mm
Calf	45 mm

2. The skin has receptors for different kinds of stimuli. Explore sensitivity to temperature, vibration, flutter, or motion.

Internet Connections

Neuroscience for Kids

http://faculty.washington.edu/chudler/introb.html
Links under the "Sensory Systems" section describe the different sensory receptors we have in our skin and take a look at pain.

* Reprinted with permission from *Principles and Standards for School Mathematics*, 2000 by the National Council of Teachers of Mathematics. All rights reserved.

SENSITIVE SKIN

Key Question

Which of the five places tested on your body is the most sensitive to touch?

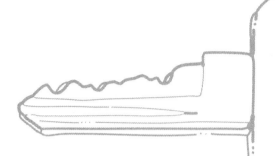

Learning Goal

Students will:

perform a two-point discrimination test on five areas of their bodies to see how sensitive different locations are to touch.

Constructing the Touch Testers

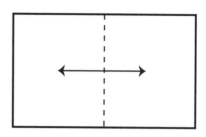

1. Fold an index card in half vertically and open it up.

2. Fold each side in to meet the center crease. Re-fold along the center crease line.

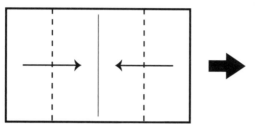 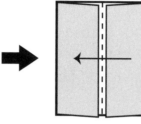 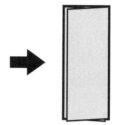

3. Tape the edges to hold the card closed. Repeat with each card for a total of eight.

4. Make two points that are 0.5 cm apart on one of the cards. Put the points near the center of the card.

5. Use a pushpin to make a hole through each of the points. Label the card with the distance that the points are apart. Repeat with the other seven distances listed below.

   1 cm   1.5 cm   2 cm   2.5 cm   3 cm   3.5 cm   4 cm

6. Straighten one arm of a paper clip so that it is perpendicular to the clip. Repeat with all the paper clips.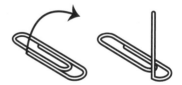

7. Put the straight arm of one paper clip into each hole on one of the cards. Arrange the paper clips so that they lie flat on the surface of the card and tape them down.

8. Turn the card over and check to see that the two arms are straight and do not flare in or out. They should still be the same distance apart as the holes. If necessary, bend them to make adjustments.

9. Do this with each card so that you have a total of eight touch testers.

© 2010 AIMS Education Foundation

 **Using the Touch Testers**

1. Work with your group. Take turns being the tester, the subject, and the recorder.
2. Each person will have his /her sensitivity to touch tested in the following five locations:
   - The tip of the index finger on the right hand
   - The inside of the left arm, halfway between the wrist and the elbow
   - The right cheek, halfway between the eye and the jaw line
   - The back of the left calf, halfway between the knee and the ankle
   - The bottom of the right foot on the heel
3. Be sure to remove your shoes and socks and pull up your sleeve and the leg of your pants if necessary. All tests must be done on bare skin.

Roles for the Experiment

Tester

1. Select one of the touch testers.
2. Touch the tester to the subject's skin in the designated area. Be very careful to do these things:
   - touch both points to the skin at the same time
   - touch the subject only with the tester points, not your hand
   - touch lightly—you should see the skin move, but not much
3. If the subject can feel two points, use a touch tester with points closer together and repeat the experiment. If the subject cannot feel two points, select a tester with the points farther apart and repeat the experiment.
4. Continue to use narrower and narrower (or wider and wider) touch testers in the same area until the subject can no longer feel two different points (or can finally feel two different points).

Subject

1. Close your eyes or look away while the tester is performing the experiment.
2. After each touch, tell the recorder whether you could feel two points or only one.
3. Remember, this is not a contest. Be honest about what you feel, and tell the tester if there was an error. (For example, if the tester did not touch you with both points at the same time.)

Recorder

1. For each trial, record the size of the tester being used (0.5 cm, 2 cm, 3.5 cm, etc.) and whether the subject could feel one or two points.
2. When all trials have been completed, circle the threshold value for each location. This is the smallest distance at which the subject was able to feel two points.

SENSITIVE SKIN

Subject: _____

Location: Cheek

Tester size	One or two points?
_____ cm	_____
_____ cm	_____
_____ cm	_____
_____ cm	_____
_____ cm	_____
_____ cm	_____

Location: Calf

Tester size	One or two points?
_____ cm	_____
_____ cm	_____
_____ cm	_____
_____ cm	_____
_____ cm	_____
_____ cm	_____

Location: Index Finger

Tester size	One or two points?
_____ cm	_____
_____ cm	_____
_____ cm	_____
_____ cm	_____
_____ cm	_____
_____ cm	_____

Location: Forearm

Tester size	One or two points?
_____ cm	_____
_____ cm	_____
_____ cm	_____
_____ cm	_____
_____ cm	_____

Location: Heel

Tester size	One or two points?
_____ cm	_____
_____ cm	_____
_____ cm	_____
_____ cm	_____
_____ cm	_____

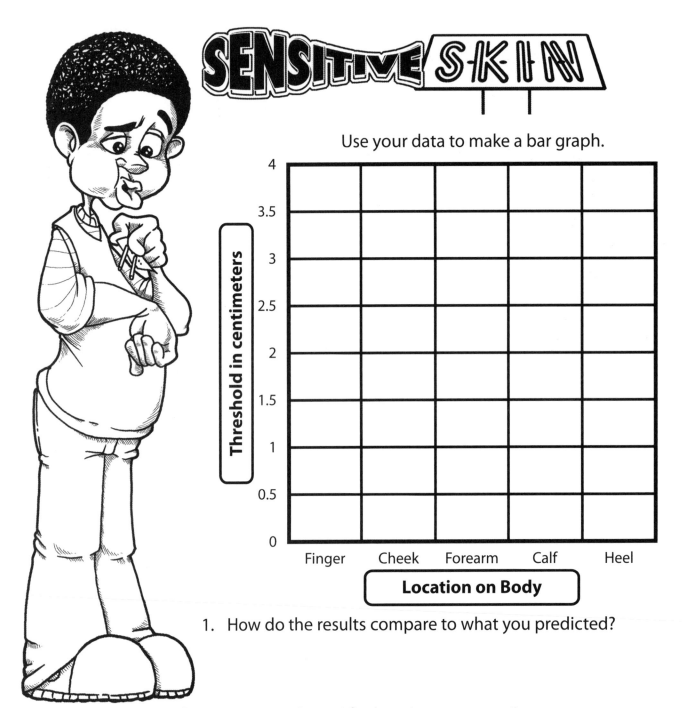

SENSITIVE SKIN

Use your data to make a bar graph.

Threshold in centimeters

(y-axis: 0, 0.5, 1, 1.5, 2, 2.5, 3, 3.5, 4)

(x-axis: Finger, Cheek, Forearm, Calf, Heel)

Location on Body

1. How do the results compare to what you predicted?

2. How do your results compare to those of others in your group?

3. Record the mode (most frequent) threshold for each of the body locations for the members of your group.

Location	Mode Threshold
Finger	cm
Cheek	cm
Forearm	cm
Calf	cm
Heel	cm

Connecting Learning

1. Which of the body parts that we tested did you predict would be most sensitive to touch? Why did you think this?

2. How did the results compare to what you expected? Did everyone have the same results?

3. According to our class graph, which of the body parts we tested is the most sensitive to touch? ...least sensitive?

4. Are there any locations that have about the same sensitivity to touch? How could we find out which is actually more sensitive?

Connecting Learning

5. Did anyone's individual results vary from the most common results in the class? What might be some reasons for any differences?

6. Do you think that you can learn to be more sensitive touch in certain locations? Explain.

7. What are you wondering now?

220

The vibrations travel from the middle ear to the inner ear. In the inner ear there is a small curled tube. It is called the cochlea. The cochlea is filled with liquid. It is also lined with microscopic hairs. The vibrations make the liquid and the hairs move.

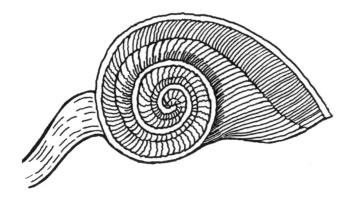

You've probably learned that we hear with our ears. But that's only part of the story. Let's take a look at how the whole process works.

This movement gets sent to the brain as nerve signals. The brain interprets the signals as sound. That's how you can hear a song on the radio or tell when someone is walking up behind you.

Here's to Ears

Think of some of the sounds you hear every day. The sound of the alarm clock, a toilet flushing, a glass of orange juice being poured, the front door closing, the school bell. Sounds are all around us all the time.

FROM HEAD TO TOE

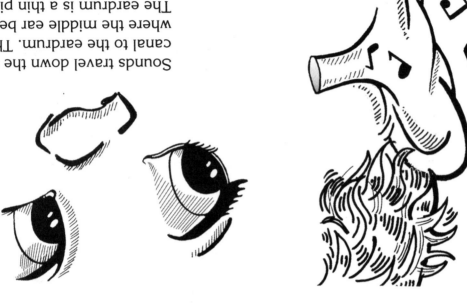

Sounds travel down the ear canal to the eardrum. This is where the middle ear begins. The eardrum is a thin piece of skin. It works like the head of a drum. Sound waves hit the eardrum and make it vibrate.

The outer ear is the part you can see. It's what sticks out from the sides of your head. It is called the pinna or auricle. The ear canal is also part of the outer ear. This is the hole that leads into the middle ear. The function of the outer ear is to collect sounds.

Behind the eardrum are three tiny bones. They are the smallest bones in your body. They are named for their shapes: the hammer, the anvil, and the stirrup. When the eardrum vibrates, these tiny bones move.

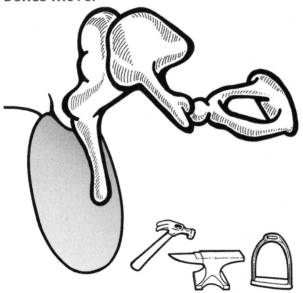

There are three parts to each of your ears—the outer ear, the middle ear, and the inner ear. Each part plays an important role in your ability to hear.

In Your Ear

Topic
Ears

Key Question
What are the parts of the ear, and where are they located?

Learning Goal
Students will work together in groups and use logic to identify the parts of the ear on a diagram.

Guiding Documents
Project 2061 Benchmark
- *Geometric figures, number sequences, graphs, diagrams, sketches, number lines, maps, and stories can be used to represent objects, events, and processes in the real world, although such representations can never be exact in every detail.*

NRC Standard
- *Specialized cells perform specialized functions in multicellular organisms. Groups of specialized cells cooperate to form a tissue, such as a muscle. Different tissues are in turn grouped together to form larger functional units, called organs. Each type of cell, tissue, and organ has a distinct structure and set of functions that serve the organism as a whole.*

NCTM Standards 2000*
- *Solve problems that arise in mathematics and in other contexts*
- *Apply and adapt a variety of appropriate strategies to solve problems*

Math
Problem solving
  logical thinking

Science
Life science
  human body
    ears

Integrated Processes
Observing
Recording
Identifying

Materials
Clue cards, one set per group
Ear diagram, one per student
Colored pencils

Background Information
Our ears are the sensory organs that allow us to hear. Our ears have three regions—outer, middle, and inner. The outer ear includes the part of the ear we can see as well as the auditory canal. The visible part of the ear is called the pinna or auricle and is responsible for collecting sounds. These sounds travel through the auditory canal to the middle ear, which begins with the eardrum, or tympanic membrane. Behind the tympanic membrane are the three smallest bones in the human body—the malleus (hammer), the incus (anvil), and the stapes (stirrup). These bones are located in the tympanic cavity—an open space in the middle ear. The malleus is connected to the tympanic membrane, and when the membrane vibrates, so does the bone. These vibrations are transferred from the malleus to the incus, and then to the stapes. The stapes is attached to the oval window, a small membrane on the cochlea. The cochlea is part of the inner ear. It is a curved snail-shaped tube filled with liquid and microscopic hairs. The vibrations set the hairs and liquid in motion and are finally transmitted to the brain by means of the cochlear nerve, where they are interpreted as sounds. The semicircular canals and the otolith organs make up the rest of the inner ear, but their function is related to equilibrium and not hearing.

Management
1. Students need to work in groups of four on this activity. If you do not have a number of students divisible by four, you can add a fifth student to some groups and two students can share a clue card.
2. Copy the clue cards onto card stock and cut them apart before doing this activity. Each group needs one set of clue cards.

Procedure
1. Have students get into their groups. Distribute one set of clue cards and colored pencils to each group and a diagram of the ear to each student.
2. Instruct each student in the group to take one clue card from the set. (If there are five students in the group, have the two of the students share one card.)

3. Inform students that the challenge is to work together as a group to correctly label all the parts of the ear diagram and then to identify which parts form the outer, middle, and inner ear.

4. Explain that every student will take turns reading the clues on his or her card. If the clue gives information that can be immediately used, that information can be recorded on the diagram. Once all of the clues have been read, they can share them as a group and revisit clues that may become more helpful once other information is known.

5. After all of the parts have been correctly labeled, have students use the colored pencils to identify the parts of the outer, middle, and inner ear by coloring them different colors. Instruct them to fill in the key so that their diagrams can be interpreted.

Connecting Learning

1. What are the three regions of the ear? [inner, middle, outer]

2. Where are the hammer, anvil, and stirrup found? [middle ear] What is their function? [transfer vibrations from eardrum to cochlea]

3. What are the parts of the ear that you can see? [The pinna, or auricle and part of the auditory canal.] What region of the ear do these parts belong to? [outer ear]

4. Why do you think they call the part of the ear with the cochlea the inner ear? [It is furthest inside your head.]

5. What do you think would happen if the hammer were not connected to the tympanic membrane? [The vibrations would not be transferred; loss of hearing would result.]

6. What is one new thing you learned from this activity?

7. What are you wondering now?

Internet Connections
KidsHealth®
http://kidshealth.org/kid/htbw/
Select the ear from the scrolling list for information on the ear including articles, diagrams, and activities.

Solutions

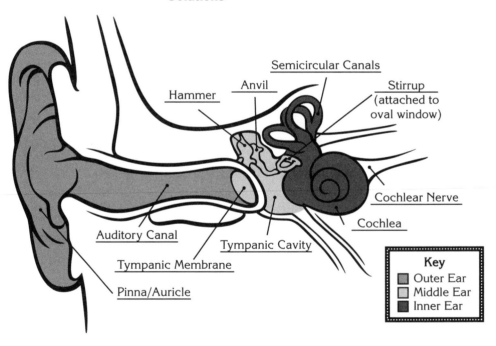

In Your Ear

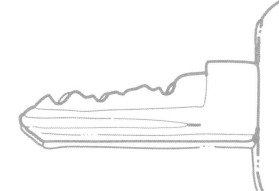

Key Question

What are the parts of the ear, and where are they located?

Learning Goal

work together in groups and use logic to identify the parts of the ear on a diagram.

In Your (Ear)

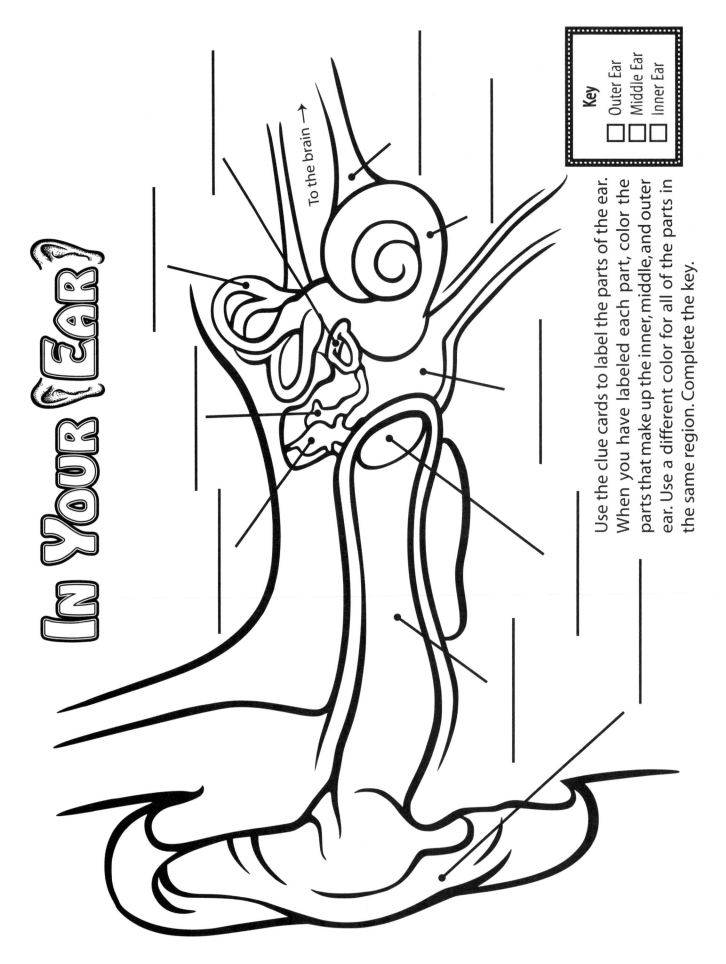

To the brain →

Key
Outer Ear
Middle Ear
Inner Ear

Use the clue cards to label the parts of the ear. When you have labeled each part, color the parts that make up the inner, middle, and outer ear. Use a different color for all of the parts in the same region. Complete the key.

In Your Ear

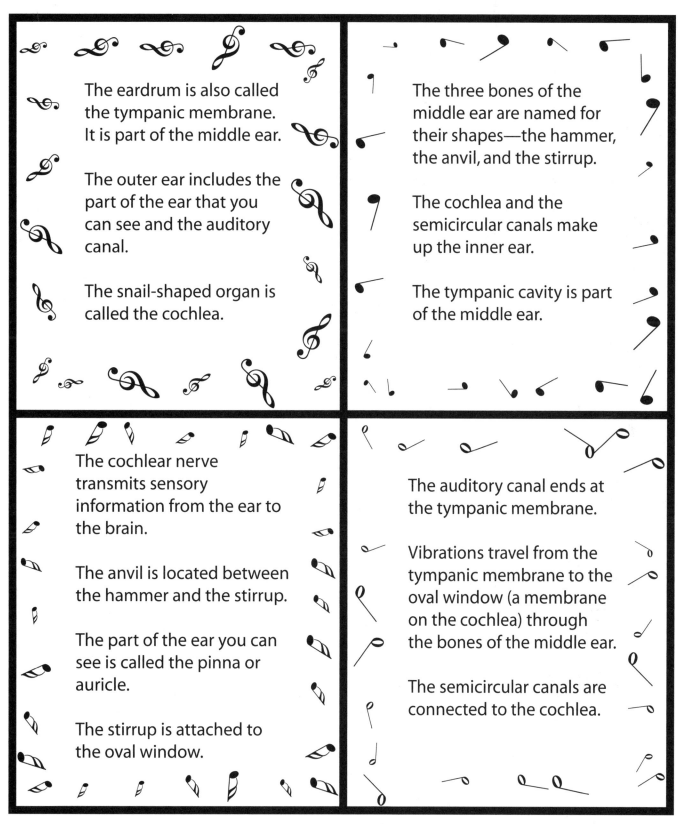

The eardrum is also called the tympanic membrane. It is part of the middle ear.

The outer ear includes the part of the ear that you can see and the auditory canal.

The snail-shaped organ is called the cochlea.

The three bones of the middle ear are named for their shapes—the hammer, the anvil, and the stirrup.

The cochlea and the semicircular canals make up the inner ear.

The tympanic cavity is part of the middle ear.

The cochlear nerve transmits sensory information from the ear to the brain.

The anvil is located between the hammer and the stirrup.

The part of the ear you can see is called the pinna or auricle.

The stirrup is attached to the oval window.

The auditory canal ends at the tympanic membrane.

Vibrations travel from the tympanic membrane to the oval window (a membrane on the cochlea) through the bones of the middle ear.

The semicircular canals are connected to the cochlea.

In Your Ear

Connecting Learning

1. What are the three regions of the ear?

2. Where are the hammer, anvil, and stirrup found? What is their function?

3. What are the parts of the ear that you can see? What region of the ear do these parts belong to?

4. Why do you think they call the part of the ear with the cochlea the inner ear?

5. What do you think would happen if the hammer were not connected to the tympanic membrane?

6. What is one new thing you learned from this activity?

7. What are you wondering now?

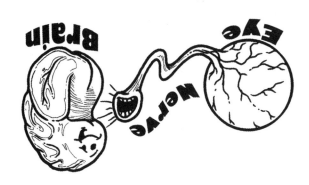

When light hits the retina, the rods and cones change the information into nerve signals. They send those signals through the optic nerve to the brain. The brain interprets those signals so you know what you are seeing.

What color is the shirt your teacher is wearing? Are there clouds in the sky right now? What is the last word on this page? To answer these questions, you need to use your eyes.

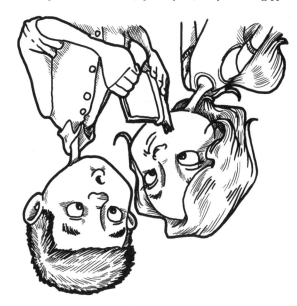

As you can see, your eyes are very complex and special. It is important to take care of them so they will serve you for years to come.

All the way in the back of your eye is the retina. The lens focuses light on the retina. The retina contains special cells called rods and cones. These cells help the retina process light.

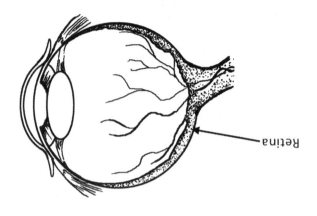

Retina

Have you ever held a table tennis ball? That's about the size of one of your eyes. Your eyes sit in eye sockets, and they are protected by your eyelids. Your eyelashes also help protect your eyes by keeping out dust and other things that don't belong.

Rods allow us to see in black, white, and shades of gray. They help us to distinguish shapes and allow us to see in very low light. Cones allow us to see color. They need more light to work. That's why you can't see colors in the dark.

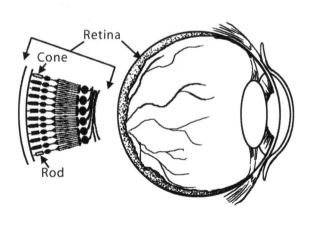

Retina

Cone

Rod

Your eyes are the sensory organs that allow you to see. They are constantly taking in information. Your brain processes this information to let you know what is going on around you. There are many parts to your eyes, and these parts all work together to help you see.

TREE

FROM HEAD TO TOE

6

The colored part of your eye is called the iris. The iris can change its shape. This controls the amount of light that goes through the pupil. The pupil is the black part in the center of your eye. It's actually a hole in your iris. Light goes through the pupil and into the inner eye.

Iris

Now look at your friend's eyes from the side. Can you see a clear dome at the front of the eye? That's the cornea. It helps the eye focus. You can think of it like the window into your eye.

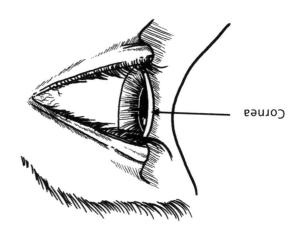

Cornea

The parts of the inner eye can't be seen without special instruments. When light goes through the pupil, it hits the lens. Just like the lens of a camera, the lens in your eye helps focus light.

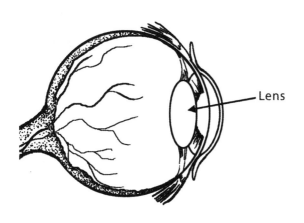

Lens

Look at a friend's eyes. Do you see the white part? That is called the sclera. It covers most of the eyeball. It is like the outer coat of the eye. If you look closely, you can see the blood vessels running through the sclera.

Sight-Seeing

Topic
Eyes

Key Question
How does light pass through the lens in the human eye and project an image onto the retina?

Learning Goals
Students will:
- construct a model of a human eye,
- pass light from a window through a hand lens onto the retina of the model, and
- observe the image of the scene outside the window as projected onto the model's retina.

Guiding Documents
Project 2061 Benchmarks
- *The brain gets signals from all parts of the body telling what is going on there. The brain also sends signals to parts of the body to influence what they do.*
- *Something can be "seen" when light waves emitted or reflected by it enter the eye—just as something can be "heard" when sound waves from it enter the ear.*
- *Geometric figures, number sequences, graphs, diagrams, sketches, number lines, maps, and stories can be used to represent objects, events, and processes in the real world, although such representations can never be exact in every detail.*

NRC Standards
- *Light interacts with matter by transmission (including refraction), absorption, or scattering (including reflection). To see an object, light from that object—emitted by or scatter from it—must enter the eye.*
- *Specialized cells perform specialized functions in multicellular organisms. Groups of specialized cells cooperate to form a tissue, such as a muscle. Different tissues are in turn grouped together to form larger functional units, called organs. Each type of cell, tissue, and organ has a distinct structure and set of functions that serve the organism as a whole.*

Science
Life science
  human body
    eyes

Integrated Processes
Observing
Comparing and contrasting
Modeling

Materials
For each student:
  colored pencils
  scissors
  glue stick
  hand lens
  ruler
  Retina pattern
  student pages

Background Information
In this activity, students use a hand lens and a paper model of a human eye to demonstrate the relationship between the light reflected from an object into the eye, through the lens, and onto the retina. They observe that the image projected onto the retina is inverted. The retinal image generates electrical signals that travel through the optic nerve to the brain where the brain processes the signals to again invert the image.

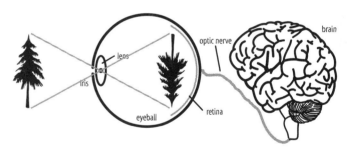

The model of the eye shows the major parts of the eye. Anatomical diagrams are generally colored for emphasis and clarity. Students are encouraged to color-code the diagram that forms the base of the model.

Key Vocabulary
Cornea: the transparent dome that sits in front of the colored part of the eye
Iris: the colored part of the eye that changes shape to control how much light enters the pupil
Lens: sits behind the iris and focuses light onto the retina
Optic nerve: sends the electrical signals generated in the eye by the light focused on the retina to the brain

Pupil: the center of the iris that lets light enter the interior of the eye

Retina: the back of the eyeball

Sclera: the white part of the eyeball

Management

1. Copy the first two student pages on card stock. Each student needs one copy of the first page and one *Retina* pattern. (The *Retina* patterns are printed three to a page.)
2. Schedule time to do the activity yourself. Doing so will help you better guide your students through the activity.
3. Hand lenses (item number 1977) and rulers (item number 1909) are available from AIMS.

Procedure

1. Review the information about the parts of the eye contained in the *Eye See* rubber band book. If students have not already read this book, have them do so.
2. Distribue the first student page and colored pencils to each student. Instruct them to color the model of the eye so that each part is a different color and to complete the key.
3. Distribute the page of instructions, a *Retina* pattern, scissors, and a glue stick to each student.
4. Have students follow the instructions to construct the model. Provide assistance as needed.
5. Distribute the final student page, a hand lens, and a ruler to each student. Demonstrate how to hold the hand lens, standing with your back to a window, so that the image of the scene outside the window is projected onto the paper retina of the model.

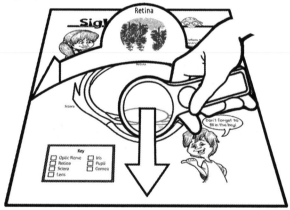

6. Allow students time to replicate this phenomenon and explore the images projected onto the models.
7. Have them complete the student page by sketching the image they saw on their model, drawing the lines representing light on the diagram, and sketching the arrow as it would appear on the retina.
8. Discuss how images appear on the retina [upside down] and what other things students learned about the eye and how it functions from this activity.

Connecting Learning

1. What are the main parts of your eye? [cornea, sclera, iris, pupil, lens, retina]
2. What is the function of the pupil? ...the iris? ...the lens? ...the retina?
3. What part on our model represented the retina? [the paper screen]
4. What part of the model represented the eye's lens? [the hand lens]
5. What did you notice about the image that appeared on the retina in your model? [It was upside down.]
6. Why don't we see things upside down if that's how they enter our eyes? [The eyes send messages to the brain, and the brain interprets the messages and turns what we see "right side up."]
7. How was your model eye like your real eye? How was it different?
8. What are you wondering now?

Internet Connections

KidsHealth®

http://kidshealth.org/kid/htbw/

Select the eyes from the scrolling list for information on the eyes including articles, diagrams, and activities.

Solutions

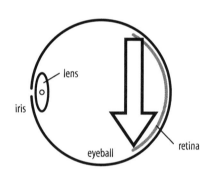

Sight-Seeing

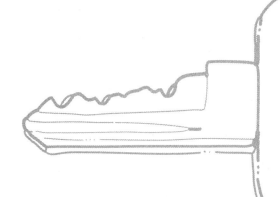

Key Question

How does light pass through the lens in the human eye and project an image onto the retina?

Learning Goals

- construct a model of a human eye,

- pass light from a window through a hand lens onto the retina of the model, and

- observe the image of the scene outside the window as projected onto the model's retina.

Sight-Seeing

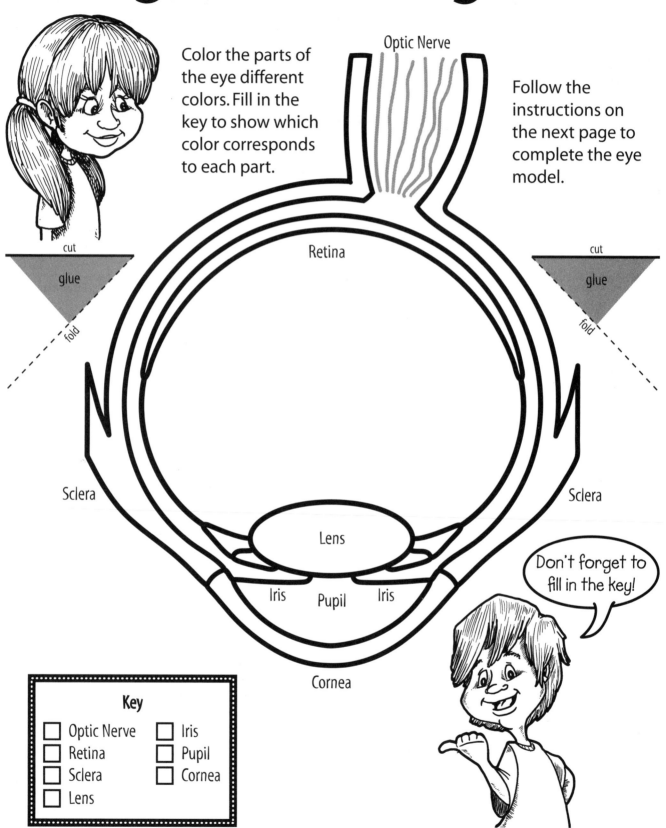

Color the parts of the eye different colors. Fill in the key to show which color corresponds to each part.

Follow the instructions on the next page to complete the eye model.

Optic Nerve

Retina

cut
glue
fold

cut
glue
fold

Sclera

Sclera

Lens

Iris   Pupil   Iris

Cornea

Don't forget to fill in the key!

Key
- ☐ Optic Nerve
- ☐ Retina
- ☐ Sclera
- ☐ Lens
- ☐ Iris
- ☐ Pupil
- ☐ Cornea

Sight-Seeing

Copy this page on card stock. Each student needs one *Retina* pattern.

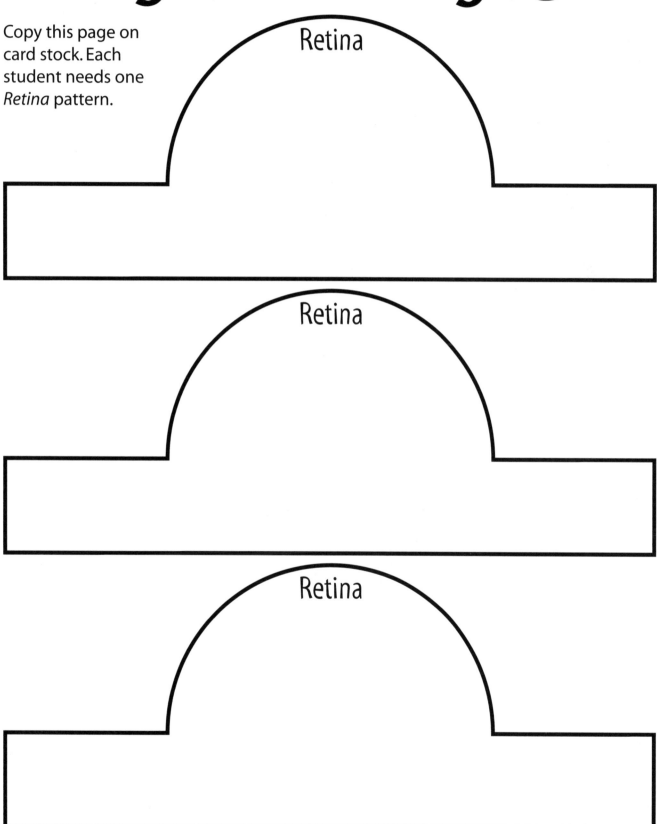

Retina

Retina

Retina

Instructions for Constructing the Eye Model

1. Cut out the *Retina* pattern.

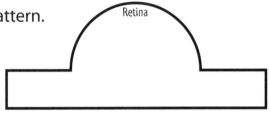

2. Cut all the way to the edge of the paper on each line that says "cut." Fold along the dashed lines all the way to the edges of the paper. This will give you two triangular tabs.

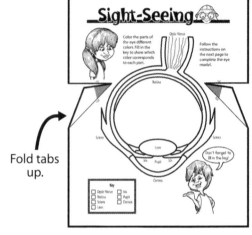

Fold tabs up.

3. Apply glue to the shaded area on the left triangular tab. Press the left end of the *Retina* pattern in place.

4. Repeat the process for the right side. The *Retina* pattern should stand vertically on the page as shown.

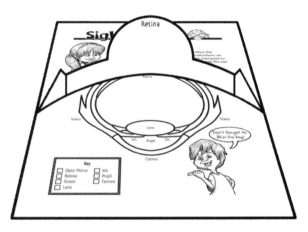

Sight-Seeing

1. Sketch what you observe on the retina of the model when you hold the hand lens in front of the model.

2. Light travels in a straight line. Use your ruler to draw the straight lines from the arrow on the left, starting with the gray guidelines, through the small circle at the center of the lens, and onto the retina. Sketch the image of the arrow as it would appear on the retina.

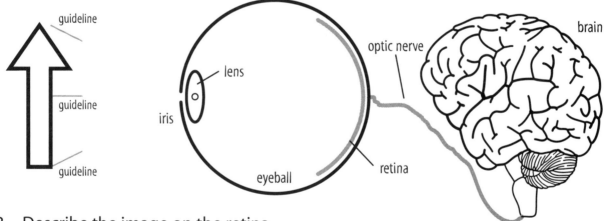

3. Describe the image on the retina.

Sight-Seeing

Connecting Learning

1. What are the main parts of your eye?

2. What is the function of the pupil? …the iris? …the lens? …the retina?

3. What part on our model represented the retina?

4. What part of the model represented the eye's lens?

5. What did you notice about the image that appeared on the retina in your model?

Sight-Seeing

Connecting Learning

6. Why don't we see things upside down if that's how they enter our eyes?

7. How was your model eye like your real eye? How was it different?

8. What are you wondering now?

NO GOAL IN SIGHT

Topic
Eyes

Key Question
What is a blind spot?

Learning Goals
Students will:
- do an activity to demonstrate that they have a blind spot, and
- understand the reason for the blind spot.

Guiding Documents
Project 2061 Benchmarks
- *Something can be "seen" when light waves emitted or reflected by it enter the eye—just as something can be "heard" when sound waves from it enter the ear.*
- *The brain gets signals from all parts of the body telling what is going on there. The brain also sends signals to parts of the body to influence what they do.*

NRC Standard
- *Light interacts with matter by transmission (including refraction), absorption, or scattering (including reflection). To see an object, light from that object—emitted by or scatter from it—must enter the eye.*

NCTM Standard 2000*
- *Select and apply techniques and tools to accurately find length, area, volume, and angle measures to appropriate levels of precision*

Math
Measurement
  length

Science
Life science
  human body
    eyes
      blind spot

Integrated Processes
Observing
Comparing and contrasting
Collecting and recording data

Materials
Metric tape measures
Student pages

Background Information
The human eye enables us to gather much information about our world. Light is bent by both the cornea and lens. This bent light passes through the pupil to the back of the eyeball (the retina). The retina contains photoreceptors called rods and cones, which are light-sensitive cells. The human eye contains approximately 100 million rods that are scattered over the retina. They are more light sensitive than are the cones. Vision in dim light is almost entirely due to the reception by the rods. Cones detect color and are used mostly in daylight. They come in three varieties determined by their sensitivity to a particular color, either red, green, or blue. These photoreceptors send their messages to the brain via axons that form the optic nerve. To exit the eyeball, these axons must pass through the retina in one place. This place is called the blind spot because it lacks receptors.

This discrepant event has the student, with one eye covered, focus on a picture of the basketball the player is holding. As the paper is moved toward the observer's face, he or she continues to focus on the basketball. The "basket," which is represented by the dot, disappears as its image falls upon the blind spot of the retina. Voila! No goal in sight!

Management
1. Each student needs his or her own copy of the student page.
2. Each pair of students needs one metric tape measure and one picture of the basketball player and basket.
3. Metric tape measures (item number 1926) are available from AIMS.

Procedure
1. Ask students if they have ever heard the phrase "blind spot." Have them share what they understand the phrase to mean. [They may know it as the spot when a passing car (or other object) cannot be seen in either the rearview or side view mirrors of a car. They may also have heard it used to describe a person who is not self-aware in a certain area. (He's a great coach, but he has a real blind spot where his own son is concerned.)]

2. Tell students that they also have a blind spot in their eyes. Have them guess what they think this means.
3. Pair students and distribute the student pages and tape measures.
4. Go over the instructions on the student page, and allow time for students to take turns finding their blind spots and measuring the distances from eye to paper.
5. Discuss the diagram of the eye on the student page and explain that the blind spot is the place where the optic nerve passes through the retina, so there are no receptors on that spot. Without receptors, there is no information for the eye to send to the brain, so nothing can be seen in that spot.

Connecting Learning
1. What happened to the "basket?" [It disappeared.]
2. Why do you think it disappeared? [It fell on the blind spot of the retina where there are no cones or rods to perceive it.]
3. How far was the paper from your face when it disappeared?
4. Was this distance the same when you tested the other eye?
5. How did your distances compare to your partners'? ...to others in the class?
6. How could you change this activity so that you would lose sight of the "basket" at a different place from your face? [change the location of the basket relative to the ball]
7. What are you wondering now?

Extension
Challenge students to create different ways to demonstrate the blind spot and to change the distance from their faces at which they notice the blind spot.

* Reprinted with permission from *Principles and Standards for School Mathematics*, 2000 by the National Council of Teachers of Mathematics. All rights reserved.

NO GOAL IN SIGHT

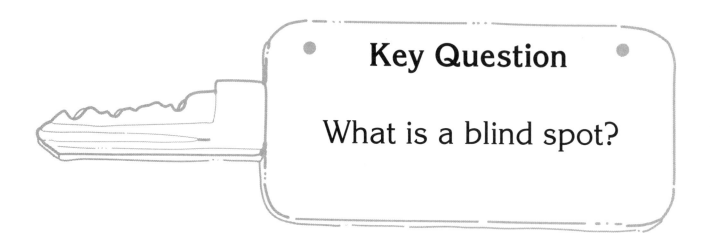

Key Question

What is a blind spot?

Learning Goals

- do an activity to demonstrate that they have a blind spot, and

- understand the reason for the blind spot.

NO GOAL IN SIGHT

NO GOAL IN SIGHT

NO GOAL IN SIGHT

- Cover your left eye.
- Hold the picture of the basketball player and "basket" (dot) at arm's length.
- Focus on the basketball the player is holding.
- Gradually bring the picture closer to your face while continuing to focus on the basketball until you lose sight of the "basket" (dot).
- Have your partner measure the distance the paper is from your eye when you lose sight of the "basket" (dot). Record.
- Repeat the same procedure covering your right eye.

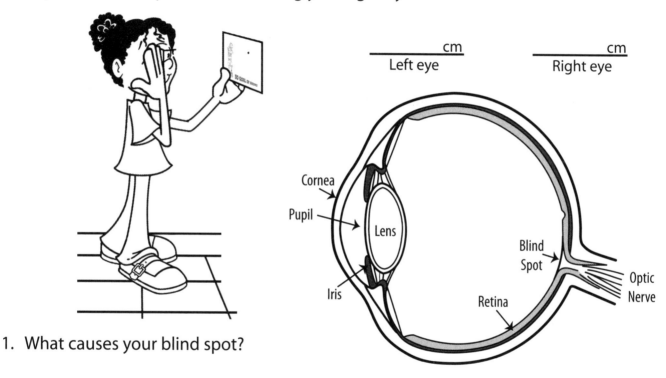

cm	cm
Left eye	Right eye

1. What causes your blind spot?

2. Was your blind spot the same distance from each eye?

3. How is the blind spot in your eye like the blind spot in a car?

NO GOAL IN SIGHT

Connecting Learning

1. What happened to the "basket?"

2. Why do you think it disappeared?

3. How far was the paper from your face when it disappeared?

4. Was this distance the same when you tested the other eye?

5. How did your distances compare to your partners'? ...to others in the class?

6. How could you change this activity so that you would lose sight of the "basket" at a different place from your face?

7. What are you wondering now?

Getting It Together

Topic
Eyes

Key Question
How does persistence of vision explain the phenomenon we see when we spin our model thaumatropes?

Learning Goals
Students will:
- learn about thaumatropes,
- make simplified versions of thaumatropes, and
- explain how persistence of vision accounts for the phenomenon that is observed.

Guiding Documents
Project 2061 Benchmark
- *Something can be "seen" when light waves emitted or reflected by it enter the eye—just as something can be "heard" when sound waves from it enter the ear.*

NRC Standard
- *Light interacts with matter by transmission (including refraction), absorption, or scattering (including reflection). To see an object, light from that object—emitted by or scatter from it—must enter the eye.*

Science
Life science
  human body
    eyes
      persistence of vision

Integrated Processes
Observing
Comparing and contrasting
Inferring

Materials
Transparent tape
Set of pictures (see *Management 1*)
Unsharpened pencils
Scissors
Colored pencils
Internet access
Student page

Background Information
A *thaumatrope* is a device invented in the 1820s that later became a popular toy. It consists of a disk (or card) with pictures on both sides. The pictures are upside-down in relation to each other. Two pieces of string are attached to the disk so that it can be spun rapidly. The spinning pictures give the impression that they have merged into one.

The thaumarope's invention is usually credited to either John Ayrton Paris or Peter Mark Roget, both British physicians in the early 1800s. *Thauma* comes from a Greek word meaning miracle or wonder; *trope* is Greek for turning; in other words, a thaumatrope is a wonder turner. Thaumatropes are considered important precursors to cinematography, especially animation.

The reason the pictures seem to merge is because the image that is projected onto your retina remains there for approximately one twenty-fifth of a second. This is referred to as persistence of vision. The card spins fast enough that the next image appears before the first image disappears. To simplify this activity, the pictures will be placed on a pencil that will be spun by rubbing the palms of the hands together.

Management
1. Copy the page with the three sets of pictures onto card stock. Make enough copies so that each student can have one set.
2. If possible, use a projection device to display the suggested website for the class to see. Otherwise, you can have multiple computers set up with students taking turns to look at the images.

Procedure
1. Load the website given in *Internet Connections* and display it for the class to see.
2. Explain that these pictures show thaumatropes, which were a popular toy in the 1800s. The cards have pictures on both sides, and when they are spun quickly using the string attached to each side, the two pictures appear to combine into one image.
3. Click on the "Flash Gallery" link and look at some of the animations.
4. Explain that students will be making their own versions of these thaumatropes and will explore the reason that they work.
5. Distribute the student page, a card set, tape, colored pencils, an unsharpened pencil, and scissors to each student.

6. Have students follow the instructions on the student page to construct their model thaumatropes.
7. Discuss the notion of persistence of vision and how this relates to the thaumatropes.

Connecting Learning

1. What did you notice about the pictures when you spun the cards?
2. How does persistence of vision explain why this happened? [The images from the cards remain on the retina for fractions of a second. Because the cards are spinning so quickly, you are "seeing" both images at the same time, causing them to appear to merge.]
3. Of what does this remind you? [frames on movie film]
4. What are you wondering now?

Extension

Challenge students to design their own pictures and see if they can get them to merge as one. To what things do they need to pay special attention?

Internet Connections

The Richard Balzer Collection
http://www.dickbalzer.com/Thaumatropes.260.0.html
This site has photographs of the fronts and backs of original thaumatropes from the 1800s. Click on the "Flash Gallery" link in the left sidebar to see the thaumatropes animated.

Getting It Together

Key Question

How does persistence of vision explain the phenomenon we see when we spin our model thaumatropes?

Learning Goals

Students will:

- learn about thaumatropes,

- make simplified versions of thaumatropes, and

- explain how persistence of vision accounts for the phenomenon that is observed.

Getting It Together

1. Cut apart and color your two cards.

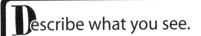

2. Tape a pencil to the back side of one of the cards. Be sure the picture on the card is oriented with its top toward the eraser end of the pencil.

3. Place the companion card on top of the pencil, picture to the outside. Be sure both cards are oriented the same way. Using three pieces of tape, seal the two sides and the top.

4. Place the pencil between the palm of your hands and rapidly rub your palms back and forth. Observe the spinning cards.

Describe what you see.

Trade cards with someone who has different pictures. Describe what you see.

Persistence of vision is a phenomenon in which an image remains on the retina for about one twenty-fifth of a second. How does persistence of vision explain what you see when you spin the cards?

Getting It Together

Connecting Learning

1. What did you notice about the pictures when you spun the cards?

2. How does persistence of vision explain why this happened?

3. Of what does this remind you?

4. What are you wondering now?

7

When these receptors are stimulated, they send a message to the brain. That message travels along a nerve called the *olfactory nerve.* The message then goes to the olfactory bulb. This is under the front of your brain.

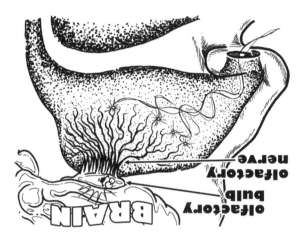

You could probably tell the difference between all of these smells with your eyes closed. But how? The answer is right in front of your face, or right on the front of your face, to be exact. It's your nose.

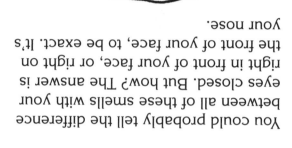

The olfactory bulb sends the message to other parts of the brain. The brain interprets the message as a smell. As you smell new things, your brain begins to learn the smells. Soon, you know what things are as soon as you smell them.

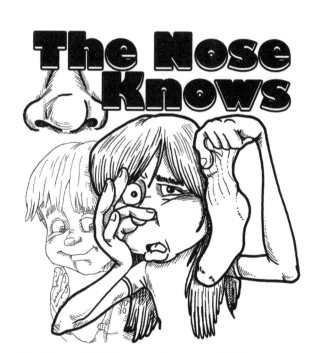

Sniff, sniff. What is that smell? Is it your brother's smelly socks? Your sister peeling an orange? Your mom baking cookies? Your dad frying bacon?

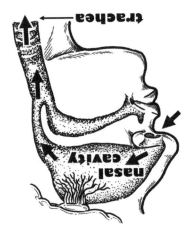

thin bone closer to your skull.
at the tip of your nose. It becomes
little wall. It is made of cartilage
the septum. The septum is like a
nose, the nostrils are separated by
allow air into your nose. Inside your
nostrils. These are the holes that
At the bottom of your nose are two

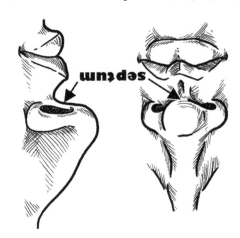

When you breathe, air comes in through
your nostrils. Then it goes to the nasal
cavity. This is a space in the middle
of your face behind your nose. From
your nasal cavity, air goes through the
trachea and down into your lungs. (The
trachea is also called the windpipe.)

It's in your nasal cavity where your
ability to smell begins. There are special
receptors in there. These receptors get
stimulated by odor molecules in the air
you breathe. The scientific name for
these receptors is *olfactory receptors*.

Your nose is one of your sensory organs.
These are the body parts that let you
see, smell, taste, touch, and hear. Your
nose, as you know, lets you smell. But
there's a little more to the story.

There's one more thing that's very important for your sense of taste, but it's not in your mouth. Your sense of smell is very closely related to your sense of taste. Your nose gives you information about food before you eat it and while you are chewing. That's why food may not taste the same to you when you have a stuffy nose.

Your ability to taste begins in your mouth. Besides your teeth, your mouth is mostly filled with your tongue. Have you ever looked closely at your tongue in the mirror? Maybe you noticed that it's not smooth. There are tiny bumps all over its surface. These bumps are called *papillae*.

Your sense of taste helps you enjoy your food, but it protects you, too. Foods that are spoiled and could make you sick often taste bad. You know not to drink sour milk because of its taste. Your tongue and your nose warn you to throw the milk out and open a new carton.

Tasty Tidbits

What is your favorite food? How does it taste? Is it sweet? Salty? How do you know?

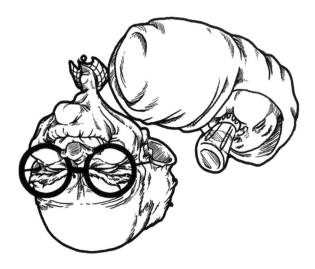

When you are born, you have about 10,000 taste buds. As you get older, some of these taste buds die. By the time you are a grandparent, you might have only 5000 taste buds.

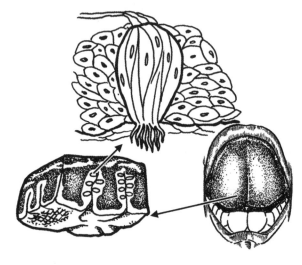

Taste buds are made up of taste cells. These cells have microscopic hairs that send messages to your brain by means of nerves. Your brain interprets the messages and tells you what you are tasting.

Your taste buds need help from something else in your mouth to work. Your spit, or saliva, is very important for tasting food. There are chemicals in foods that give them taste. These chemicals have to be dissolved in saliva for your taste cells to detect the flavor.

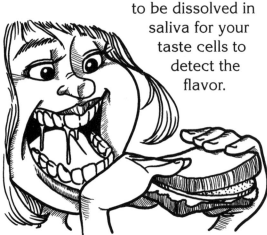

These bumps help move the food around when you are chewing. They also contain your taste buds. Taste buds can detect different flavors like sweet, salty, bitter, and sour.

FROM HEAD TO TOE

© 2010 AIMS Education Foundation

Topic
Senses of taste and smell

Key Question
How does your sense of smell affect your sense of taste?

Learning Goal
Students will recognize that the senses of smell and taste are closely related by performing experiments designed to fool the sense of taste.

Guiding Document
NRC Standard
- *Specialized cells perform specialized functions in multicellular organisms. Groups of specialized cells cooperate to form a tissue, such as a muscle. Different tissues are in turn grouped together to form larger functional units, called organs. Each type of cell, tissue, and organ has a distinct structure and set of functions that serve the organism as a whole.*

Science
Life science
  human body
    senses

Integrated Processes
Observing
Comparing and contrasting
Recording
Relating

Materials
Apples (see *Management 2*)
Two onions (see *Management 3*)
Coffee
Warm water
Drinking straws
Zipper-type plastic bags
Sharp knife
Paper plates
Styrofoam cups

Background Information
Our senses of smell and taste are closely related. We smell foods before we eat them, and the aroma has a significant impact on what we taste. In fact, strong odors can actually interfere with the ability to accurately detect the flavor of what is being eaten.

In this activity, students will taste an apple while simulatneously smelling an onion and drink water while smelling coffee. They will experience how the tastes of the apple and the water are affected by what they are smelling as they are eating/drinking.

Management
1. You will need to have four stations set up around the room—two for the coffee and two for the onions. Try to have the coffee stations and the onion stations as far apart as possible. This will help reduce the overlap of smells.
2. Peel the apples and cut them into small, bite-sized chunks. Cut enough apples so that each student can have two pieces. Divide the apples between two plates and put one plate at each of the onion smelling stations.
3. If possible, use a white onion, as these tend to have the strongest odor and the color will match the color of the apple. Cut the onions in quarters and seal each quarter in a zipper-type plastic bag. Put four bags at each of the onion smelling stations.
4. Put a small amount of coffee in eight Styrofoam cups. Fill additional cups with an inch or two of warm water so that each student can have one. Put four cups of coffee and half of the cups of warm water at each coffee smelling station.
5. Each student needs his or her own drinking straw with which to sip the water while smelling the coffee. Put enough straws at each of the coffee smelling stations for each student to have his or her own.
6. Have students wash their hands with soap and water before and after handling the food.

Procedure
1. Ask students to think of some of their favorite smells. Record their responses on the board. Ask if any of these smells makes them hungry when they smell it, and why. [Smells that are associated with food often produce a sensation of hunger or a desire for that particular food.]

2. Invite students to share what they know about how the sense of smell is related to the sense of taste. Ask if anyone has had the experience of not being able to taste food well when they were stuffed up.

3. Explain that students will be performing an experiment to see how the sense of smell can affect the sense of taste. They will be drinking water while smelling coffee and eating an apple while smelling an onion.

4. Show students the four stations. Distribute the student page and go over the procedure for each station.

5. Divide students into four groups and have each group go to one of the stations. Identify the station to which each group will go when all of their group members have completed the first experiment.

6. Allow time for students to perform both experiments. Have students return to their seats and record their observations.

7. Discuss how what they were smelling affected their sense of taste in each experiment.

Connecting Learning

1. What did you experience when you ate the apple while smelling the onion? How did this compare to eating the apple without smelling the onion?

2. What did you experience when you drank water while smelling coffee? How did this compare to drinking water without smelling coffee?

3. Which of the experiments produced the most noticeable effect? Why do you think this might be?

4. What can you conclude about how the sense of smell and the sense of taste are related?

5. What are you wondering now?

Extensions

1. Experiment with other foods and smells to see what combinations produce the most drastic effects.

2. See how the senses of sight and taste are related by creating discrepant events. For example, does orange flavored punch that is colored purple still taste like orange? Does vanilla frosting that has been colored brown taste like chocolate?

Internet Connections

KidsHealth®
http://kidshealth.org/kid/htbw/
Select the tongue from the scrolling list for information on the tongue including articles, diagrams, and activities.

Key Question

How does your sense of smell affect your sense of taste?

Learning Goal

Students will:

recognize that the senses of smell and taste are closely related by performing experiments designed to fool the sense of taste.

Tricky Tastes

Onion Smelling Station

1. Open a bag with the onion and hold it to your nose.
2. Take one piece of apple and eat it while smelling the onion.
3. Keep the onion up to your nose until you are done chewing and swallowing.
4. Close the bag of onion and taste a second piece of apple.
5. Wash your hands and record your observations.

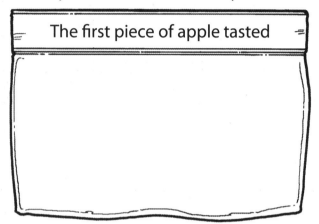

The first piece of apple tasted	The second piece of apple tasted

Coffee Smelling Station

1. Take a drinking straw and put it in a cup of water.
2. Hold a cup of coffee to your nose and breathe deeply while taking a sip of water.
3. Keep smelling the coffee until you are done swallowing.
4. Put down the coffee and take another sip of water.
5. Throw away your straw and record your observations.

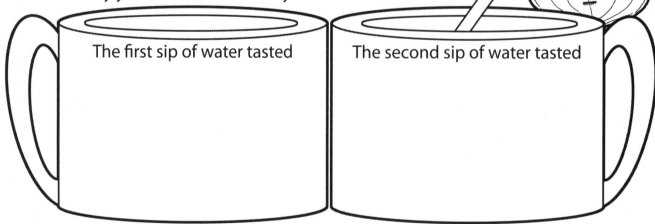

The first sip of water tasted	The second sip of water tasted

What can you conclude about how smell and taste are related?

Connecting Learning

1. What did you experience when you ate the apple while smelling the onion? How did this compare to eating the apple without smelling the onion?

2. What did you experience when you drank water while smelling coffee? How did this compare to drinking water without smelling coffee?

3. Which of the experiments produced the most noticeable effect? Why do you think this might be?

4. What can you conclude about how the sense of smell and the sense of taste are related?

5. What are you wondering now?

SYSTEM OVERLAY CONSTRUCTION

SYSTEM OVERLAY CONSTRUCTION
SYSTEM OVERLAY CONSTRUCTION

Urinary, Digestive, and Circulatory Systems

Copy the page showing the three systems onto transparency film. Copy the body page on plain paper or card stock. Each student will need a copy of both pages.

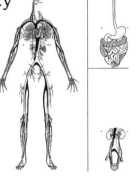

Direct students to cut the systems apart along the solid lines.

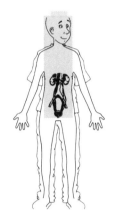

Have students place the urinary system on the illustration of the child. Tell them to align the two black dots. Have students put a small (1-inch) piece of tape along the top side of the transparency film.

Have students fold the urinary system transparency up out of the way.

Now have students align the digestive system by matching the two black dots. Have them tape this on the left side in the same manner as the urinary system.

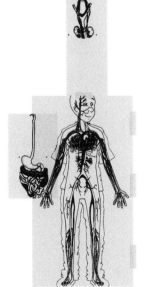

Have students fold the digestive system transparency to the left out of the way.

Direct students to take the circulatory system and align it by matching the two black dots. Have them tape the right edge of the transparency to the paper.

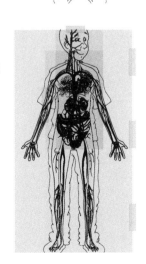

When constructed this way, students can see the placement of the individual systems, or they can look at the relationships of all the systems.

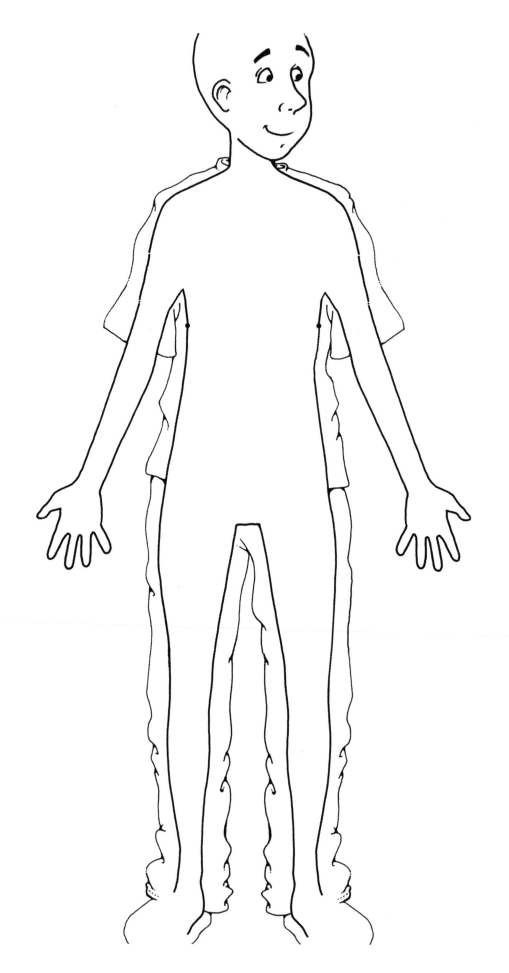

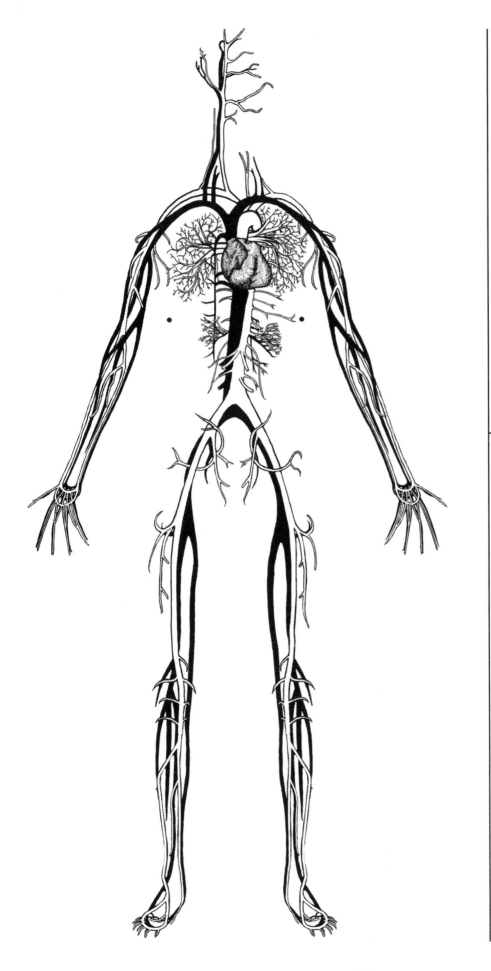
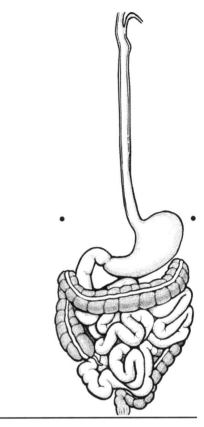
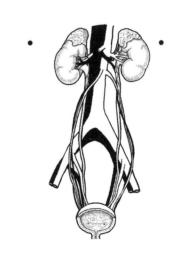

Topic
Human body

Key Question
What information can you find about the human body and its organs from the KidsHealth® website?

Learning Goal
Students will participate in an Internet scavenger hunt where they find answers to specific questions about the human body from a website.

Guiding Documents
Project 2061 Benchmarks

- *Like other animals, human beings have body systems for obtaining and providing energy, defense, reproduction, and the coordination of body functions.*
- *By breathing, people take in the oxygen they need to live.*
- *Skin protects the body from harmful substances and other organisms and from drying out.*
- *The brain gets signals from all parts of the body telling what is going on there. The brain also sends signals to parts of the body to influence what they do.*
- *From food, people obtain energy and materials for body repair and growth. The undigestible parts of food are eliminated.*
- *For the body to use food for energy and building materials, the food must first be digested into molecules that are absorbed and transported to cells.*
- *To burn food for the release of energy stored in it, oxygen must be supplied to cells, and carbon dioxide removed. Lungs take in oxygen for the combustion of food and they eliminate the carbon dioxide produced. The urinary system disposes of dissolved waste molecules, the intestinal tract removes solid wastes, and the skin and lungs rid the body of heat energy. The circulatory system moves all these substances to or from cells where they are needed or produced, responding to changing demands.*

NRC Standards

- *The human organism has systems for digestion, respiration, reproduction, circulation, excretion, movement, control, and coordination, and for protection from disease. These systems interact with one another.*

- *Specialized cells perform specialized functions in multicellular organisms. Groups of specialized cells cooperate to form a tissue, such as a muscle. Different tissues are in turn grouped together to form larger functional units, called organs. Each type of cell, tissue, and organ has a distinct structure and set of functions that serve the organism as a whole.*

Math
Graphing
  bar graph
Whole number operations

Science
Life science
  human body

Technology
Internet

Integrated Processes
Observing
Comparing and contrasting
Collecting and recording data

Materials
Computers with Internet access
Student pages
Science journals (see *Management 7*)

Background Information
The human body is made up of organs and organ systems. These systems work together to keep our bodies functioning properly. This activity is designed as a culminating experience to a study on the human body. Students will search for answers to a variety of questions about body parts and their functions on a website. While they may already know the answers to some of the questions, time spent exploring the information and resources on the website will give them additional knowledge and potentially inspire them to study some of the topics more in-depth.

Management
1. You will need multiple computers with Internet access in order for students to complete this activity. If students have Internet access at home, they can also work on this activity outside of school.
2. Bookmark the following URL on the school computers students will be using:
   http://kidshealth.org/kid/htbw/

3. Students can work individually (if you have enough computers) or in small groups.

4. Plan to have students spend time over a period of several days to a week to look for the answers to the questions. To make it fair, all students/groups should have the same amount of time.

5. It is recommended that you spend time yourself finding the answers to the questions before doing this activity with students. This will familiarize you with the website and allow you to give help and suggestions as students are searching.

6. Students will be able to answer some of the questions based on prior knowledge; however, they should be encouraged to look for each answer on the website to see what additional information can be found about the organs and body parts being studied.

7. If students do not have science journals, they can record their answers on notebook paper.

Procedure

1. Ask students if they have ever been on a scavenger hunt. Have some students describe how a scavenger hunt works and what its purpose is. [You have a list of items. You have a certain amount of time to get as many of the items as you can (without buying them).]

2. Explain that students will be going on a kind of Internet scavenger hunt. Rather than a list of items, they will be given a page of questions. They will have a certain amount of time to find answers to as many of the questions as they can by looking at the information on the KidsHealth® website.

3. Divide students into groups (if necessary) and give each group (or student) a copy of the page of questions and their science journals.

4. Have students go to the computers and begin to search for answers to the questions. Inform them that the completeness of the answers is important.

5. At the end of several days when students have had time to spend looking for answers, distribute the points recording page.

6. Go through the questions one at a time (see *Solutions*) and have students share the answers they were able to find. For each question, have them mark whether their answer was right, wrong/no answer, or incomplete. Incomplete answers receive partial points designated for the question.

7. If there were any questions for which no students were able to find answers, give them additional time at the computers to find those answers, or work together as a class to find the answers.

8. Have students total their points and graph the data. Discuss various search strategies used.

Connecting Learning

1. What new or interesting facts about the human body did you discover while you were searching for answers?

2. What did you enjoy most about the KidsHealth® website?

3. What strategies did you use to find the answers to your questions?

4. Do you think your strategies were effective? Justify your response.

5. What was the point range for the students/groups in the class? What number of points was most common?

6. Did anyone or any group find answers to all of the questions?

7. What are you wondering now?

Solutions

Some questions require more in-depth responses than others. For these questions, you can award students partial points for incomplete answers.

1. Which organ acts as the control center of the body? [the brain]

2. To which body system do your lungs belong? [respiratory system]

3. How many bones are there in an adult's body? [206]

4. How long does food spend in the small intestines? [as much as four hours]

5. Where does urine go when it leaves the kidneys? [the bladder]

6. How do messages get from your eyes to your brain? [the optic nerve]

7. How long does it take for your heart to pump blood throughout your body? [less than 60 seconds]

8. What body part has outer, middle, and inner parts? [the ear]

9. What muscle is about the size of your fist? [the heart]

10. What organ is a stretchy sack shaped like the letter "J"? [the stomach]

11. What are the three kinds of muscles in the body? [smooth, skeletal, and cardiac]

12. What are the areas of the heart called, and how many are there? [There are four chambers in the heart. The top two chambers are called atria, and the bottom two chambers are called ventricles.]

13. What are the jobs of the stomach? [food storage, food break down, transferring of food to small intestine]

14. What are the functions of the cerebrum? [voluntary muscle control, memory, reasoning, thinking]

15. How does the pancreas help with digestion? [The pancreas secretes juices that help digest fats and protein.]

16. Which intestine is longer—large or small? How do their lengths compare? [The small intestine is much longer—about 22 feet in an adult, compared to about five feet for the large intestine.]

17. What are some examples of voluntary muscles? [Answers will vary. Possibilities include deltoids, pectorals, abdominals, biceps, triceps, quadriceps, and gluteus maximus.]

18. What is the largest organ in your body? [the skin] List three interesting facts about this organ. [Answers will vary.]

19. What are the microscopic hairs in your taste buds called, and what do they do? [Microvilli send messages to the brain, and the brain interprets the messages to identify tastes.]

20. What part of your body acts like a cage, and what does it protect? [The ribs protect the heart, lungs, and liver.]

21. Which organ is about the size of a football when you are full-grown? [the liver] What are its three main purposes? [removal of toxins from the blood, bile production, and glycogen storage]

22. Which organs are shaped like beans, and what do they do? [The kidneys are bean-shaped, and they filter waste from the blood and produce urine.]

23. Where can you find the olfactory epithelium? [the nasal cavity] What is its purpose? [It contains receptors that sense odor molecules in the air.]

24. Where can you find alveoli, and about how many are there in your body? [Alveoli are found in the lungs, and there are about 600 million of them.]

25. Where are your sebaceous glands, and why are they important? [They are located in the dermis layer of the skin. They produce the natural oil (sebum) that keeps the skin waterproof, lubricated, and protected.]

Key Question

What information can you find about the human body and its organs from the KidsHealth® website?

Learning Goal

participate in an Internet scavenger hunt where they find answers to specific questions about the human body from a website.

Human Body Hunt

You are going on an Internet scavenger hunt! Your job is to learn about the human body. You will get your information from the KidsHealth® website (http://kidshealth.org/kid/htbw/).

Find answers to as many of the questions as you can. The questions have point values. Questions that are more difficult or require more detailed answers are worth more points. Use your science journal or notebook paper to record your answers.

1. Which organ acts as the control center of the body? (2 points)
2. To which body system do your lungs belong? (2 points)
3. How many bones are there in an adult's body? (2 points)
4. How long does food spend in the small intestines? (2 points)
5. Where does urine go when it leaves the kidneys? (2 points)
6. How do messages get from your eyes to your brain? (2 points)
7. How long does it take for your heart to pump blood throughout your body? (2 points)
8. What body part has outer, middle, and inner parts? (2 points)
9. What muscle is about the size of your fist? (2 points)
10. What organ is a stretchy sack shaped like the letter "J"? (2 points)
11. What are the three kinds of muscles in the body? (3 points)
12. What are the areas of the heart called, and how many are there? (3 points)
13. What are the jobs of the stomach? (3 points)
14. What are the functions of the cerebrum? (3 points)
15. How does the pancreas help with digestion? (3 points)
16. Which intestine is longer—large or small? How do their lengths compare? (3 points)
17. What are some examples of voluntary muscles? (3 points)
18. What is the largest organ in your body? List three interesting facts about this organ. (4 points)
19. What are the microscopic hairs in your taste buds called, and what do they do? (4 points)
20. What part of your body acts like a cage, and what does it protect? (4 points)
21. Which organ is about the size of a football when you are full-grown? What are its three main purposes? (4 points)
22. Which organs are shaped like beans, and what do they do? (4 points)
23. Where can you find the olfactory epithelium? What is its purpose? (5 points)
24. Where can you find alveoli, and about how many are there in your body? (5 points)
25. Where are your sebaceous glands, and why are they important? (5 points)

Human Body Hunt

	Right	Wrong/ No answer	Incomplete	
Question 1	☐	☐	☐	_____ points
Question 2	☐	☐	☐	_____ points
Question 3	☐	☐	☐	_____ points
Question 4	☐	☐	☐	_____ points
Question 5	☐	☐	☐	_____ points
Question 6	☐	☐	☐	_____ points
Question 7	☐	☐	☐	_____ points
Question 8	☐	☐	☐	_____ points
Question 9	☐	☐	☐	_____ points
Question 10	☐	☐	☐	_____ points
Question 11	☐	☐	☐	_____ points
Question 12	☐	☐	☐	_____ points
Question 13	☐	☐	☐	_____ points
Question 14	☐	☐	☐	_____ points
Question 15	☐	☐	☐	_____ points
Question 16	☐	☐	☐	_____ points
Question 17	☐	☐	☐	_____ points
Question 18	☐	☐	☐	_____ points
Question 19	☐	☐	☐	_____ points
Question 20	☐	☐	☐	_____ points
Question 21	☐	☐	☐	_____ points
Question 22	☐	☐	☐	_____ points
Question 23	☐	☐	☐	_____ points
Question 24	☐	☐	☐	_____ points
Question 25	☐	☐	☐	_____ points

Total points _____

Human Body Hunt

Number of Students/Groups	1-5	6-10	11-15	16-20	21-25	26-30	31-35	36-40	41-45	46-50	51-55	56-60	61-65	66-70	71-76
15															
14															
13															
12															
11															
10															
9															
8															
7															
6															
5															
4															
3															
2															
1															

Point Total

Number of Students/Groups

Connecting Learning

1. What new or interesting facts about the human body did you discover while you were searching for answers?

2. What did you enjoy most about the KidsHealth® website?

3. What strategies did you use to find the answers to your questions?

4. Do you think your strategies were effective? Justify your response.

5. What was the point range for the students/groups in the class? What number of points was most common?

Connecting Learning

6. Did anyone or any group find answers to all of the questions?

7. What are you wondering now?

The AIMS Program

AIMS is the acronym for "Activities Integrating Mathematics and Science." Such integration enriches learning and makes it meaningful and holistic. AIMS began as a project of Fresno Pacific University to integrate the study of mathematics and science in grades K-9, but has since expanded to include language arts, social studies, and other disciplines.

AIMS is a continuing program of the non-profit AIMS Education Foundation. It had its inception in a National Science Foundation funded program whose purpose was to explore the effectiveness of integrating mathematics and science. The project directors, in cooperation with 80 elementary classroom teachers, devoted two years to a thorough field-testing of the results and implications of integration.

The approach met with such positive results that the decision was made to launch a program to create instructional materials incorporating this concept. Despite the fact that thoughtful educators have long recommended an integrative approach, very little appropriate material was available in 1981 when the project began. A series of writing projects ensued, and today the AIMS Education Foundation is committed to continuing the creation of new integrated activities on a permanent basis.

The AIMS program is funded through the sale of books, products, and professional-development workshops, and through proceeds from the Foundation's endowment. All net income from programs and products flows into a trust fund administered by the AIMS Education Foundation. Use of these funds is restricted to support of research, development, and publication of new materials. Writers donate all their rights to the Foundation to support its ongoing program. No royalties are paid to the writers.

The rationale for integration lies in the fact that science, mathematics, language arts, social studies, etc., are integrally interwoven in the real world, from which it follows that they should be similarly treated in the classroom where students are being prepared to live in that world. Teachers who use the AIMS program give enthusiastic endorsement to the effectiveness of this approach.

Science encompasses the art of questioning, investigating, hypothesizing, discovering, and communicating. Mathematics is a language that provides clarity, objectivity, and understanding. The language arts provide us with powerful tools of communication. Many of the major contemporary societal issues stem from advancements in science and must be studied in the context of the social sciences. Therefore, it is timely that all of us take seriously a more holistic method of educating our students. This goal motivates all who are associated with the AIMS Program. We invite you to join us in this effort.

Meaningful integration of knowledge is a major recommendation coming from the nation's professional science and mathematics associations. The American Association for the Advancement of Science in *Science for All Americans* strongly recommends the integration of mathematics, science, and technology. The National Council of Teachers of Mathematics places strong emphasis on applications of mathematics found in science investigations. AIMS is fully aligned with these recommendations.

Extensive field testing of AIMS investigations confirms these beneficial results:

1. Mathematics becomes more meaningful, hence more useful, when it is applied to situations that interest students.
2. The extent to which science is studied and understood is increased when mathematics and science are integrated.
3. There is improved quality of learning and retention, supporting the thesis that learning which is meaningful and relevant is more effective.
4. Motivation and involvement are increased dramatically as students investigate real-world situations and participate actively in the process.

We invite you to become part of this classroom teacher movement by using an integrated approach to learning and sharing any suggestions you may have. The AIMS Program welcomes you!

AIMS Education Foundation Programs

When you host an AIMS workshop for elementary and middle school educators, you will know your teachers are receiving effective, usable training they can apply in their classrooms immediately.

AIMS Workshops are Designed for Teachers
- Correlated to your state standards;
- Address key topic areas, including math content, science content, and process skills;
- Provide practice of activity-based teaching;
- Address classroom management issues and higher-order thinking skills;
- Give you AIMS resources; and
- Offer optional college (graduate-level) credits for many courses.

AIMS Workshops Fit District/Administrative Needs
- Flexible scheduling and grade-span options;
- Customized (one-, two-, or three-day) workshops meet specific schedule, topic, state standards, and grade-span needs;
- Prepackaged four-day workshops for in-depth math and science training available (includes all materials and expenses);
- Sustained staff development is available for which workshops can be scheduled throughout the school year;
- Eligible for funding under the Title I and Title II sections of No Child Left Behind; and
- Affordable professional development—consecutive-day workshops offer considerable savings.

University Credit—Correspondence Courses
AIMS offers correspondence courses through a partnership with Fresno Pacific University.
- Convenient distance-learning courses—you study at your own pace and schedule. No computer or Internet access required!

Introducing AIMS State-Specific Science Curriculum
Developed to meet 100% of your state's standards, AIMS' State-Specific Science Curriculum gives students the opportunity to build content knowledge, thinking skills, and fundamental science processes.
- Each grade-specific module has been developed to extend the AIMS approach to full-year science programs. Modules can be used as a complete curriculum or as a supplement to existing materials.
- Each standards-based module includes math, reading, hands-on investigations, and assessments.

Like all AIMS resources, these modules are able to serve students at all stages of readiness, making these a great value across the grades served in your school.

For current information regarding the programs described above, please complete the following form and mail it to: P.O. Box 8120, Fresno, CA 93747.

Information Request

Please send current information on the items checked:

____ *Basic Information Packet* on AIMS materials

____ Hosting information for AIMS workshops

____ AIMS State-Specific Science Curriculum

Name: _____

Phone:_____ E-mail:_____

Address: _____
Street   City   State   Zip

Magazine

YOUR K-9 MATH AND SCIENCE
CLASSROOM ACTIVITIES RESOURCE

The AIMS Magazine is your source for standards-based, hands-on math and science investigations. Each issue is filled with teacher-friendly, ready-to-use activities that engage students in meaningful learning.

- *Four issues each year (fall, winter, spring, and summer).*

Current issue is shipped with all past issues within that volume.

| 1825 | Volume XXV | 2010-2011 | $19.95 |
| 1826 | Volume XXVI | 2011-2012 | $19.95 |

Two-Volume Combinations

| M20911 | Volumes XXIV & XXV | 2009-2011 | $34.95 |
| M21012 | Volumes XXV & XXVI | 2010-2012 | $34.95 |

Complete volumes available for purchase:

1802	Volume II	1987-1988	$19.95
1804	Volume IV	1989-1990	$19.95
1805	Volume V	1990-1991	$19.95
1807	Volume VII	1992-1993	$19.95
1808	Volume VIII	1993-1994	$19.95
1809	Volume IX	1994-1995	$19.95
1810	Volume X	1995-1996	$19.95
1811	Volume XI	1996-1997	$19.95
1812	Volume XII	1997-1998	$19.95
1813	Volume XIII	1998-1999	$19.95
1814	Volume XIV	1999-2000	$19.95
1815	Volume XV	2000-2001	$19.95
1816	Volume XVI	2001-2002	$19.95
1817	Volume XVII	2002-2003	$19.95
1818	Volume XVIII	2003-2004	$19.95
1819	Volume XIX	2004-2005	$19.95
1820	Volume XX	2005-2006	$19.95
1821	Volume XXI	2006-2007	$19.95
1822	Volume XXII	2007-2008	$19.95
1823	Volume XXIII	2008-2009	$19.95
1824	Volume XXIV	2009-2010	$19.95

Volumes II to XIX include 10 issues.

Call 1.888.733.2467 or go to www.aimsedu.org

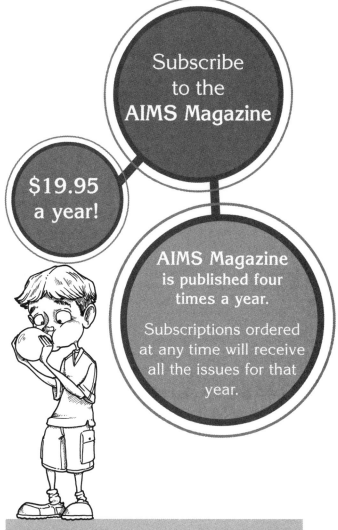

Subscribe to the AIMS Magazine

$19.95 a year!

AIMS Magazine is published four times a year.

Subscriptions ordered at any time will receive all the issues for that year.

AIMS Online—www.aimsedu.org

To see all that AIMS has to offer, check us out on the Internet at www.aimsedu.org. At our website you can preview and purchase AIMS books and individual activities, learn about State-Specific Science and Essential Math, explore professional development workshops and online learning opportunities, search our activities database, buy manipulatives and other classroom resources, and download free resources including articles, puzzles, and sample AIMS activities.

AIMS E-mail Specials
While visiting the AIMS website, sign up for our FREE e-mail newsletter with subscriber-only specials. You'll also receive advance notice of new products.

Sign up today!

AIMS Program Publications

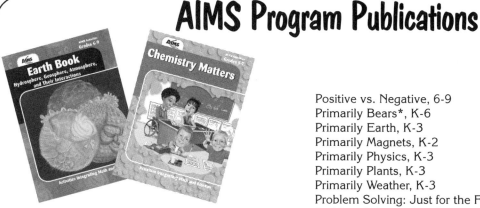

Actions With Fractions, 4-9
The Amazing Circle, 4-9
Awesome Addition and Super Subtraction, 2-3
Bats Incredible! 2-4
Brick Layers II, 4-9
The Budding Botanist, 3-6
Chemistry Matters, 5-7
Counting on Coins, K-2
Cycles of Knowing and Growing, 1-3
Crazy About Cotton, 3-7
Critters, 2-5
Earth Book, 6-9
Electrical Connections, 4-9
Exploring Environments, K-6
Fabulous Fractions, 3-6
Fall Into Math and Science*, K-1
Field Detectives, 3-6
Finding Your Bearings, 4-9
Floaters and Sinkers, 5-9
From Head to Toe, 5-9
Glide Into Winter With Math and Science*, K-1
Gravity Rules! 5-12
Hardhatting in a Geo-World, 3-5
Historical Connections in Mathematics, Vol. I, 5-9
Historical Connections in Mathematics, Vol. II, 5-9
Historical Connections in Mathematics, Vol. III, 5-9
It's About Time, K-2
It Must Be A Bird, Pre-K-2
Jaw Breakers and Heart Thumpers, 3-5
Looking at Geometry, 6-9
Looking at Lines, 6-9
Machine Shop, 5-9
Magnificent Microworld Adventures, 6-9
Marvelous Multiplication and Dazzling Division, 4-5
Math + Science, A Solution, 5-9
Mathematicians are People, Too
Mathematicians are People, Too, Vol. II
Mostly Magnets, 3-6
Movie Math Mania, 6-9
Multiplication the Algebra Way, 6-8
Out of This World, 4-8
Paper Square Geometry:
    The Mathematics of Origami, 5-12
Puzzle Play, 4-8
Popping With Power, 3-5

Positive vs. Negative, 6-9
Primarily Bears*, K-6
Primarily Earth, K-3
Primarily Magnets, K-2
Primarily Physics, K-3
Primarily Plants, K-3
Primarily Weather, K-3
Problem Solving: Just for the Fun of It! 4-9
Problem Solving: Just for the Fun of It! Book Two, 4-9
Proportional Reasoning, 6-9
Ray's Reflections, 4-8
Sensational Springtime, K-2
Sense-able Science, K-1
Shapes, Solids, and More: Concepts in Geometry, 2-3
The Sky's the Limit, 5-9
Soap Films and Bubbles, 4-9
Solve It! K-1: Problem-Solving Strategies, K-1
Solve It! 2nd: Problem-Solving Strategies, 2
Solve It! 3rd: Problem-Solving Strategies, 3
Solve It! 4th: Problem-Solving Strategies, 4
Solve It! 5th: Problem-Solving Strategies, 5
Solving Equations: A Conceptual Approach, 6-9
Spatial Visualization, 4-9
Spills and Ripples, 5-12
Spring Into Math and Science*, K-1
Statistics and Probability, 6-9
Through the Eyes of the Explorers, 5-9
Under Construction, K-2
Water, Precious Water, 4-6
Weather Sense: Temperature, Air Pressure, and Wind, 4-5
Weather Sense: Moisture, 4-5
What's Next, Volume 1, 4-12
What's Next, Volume 2, 4-12
What's Next, Volume 3, 4-12
Winter Wonders, K-2

Essential Math
Area Formulas for Parallelograms, Triangles, and Trapezoids, 6-8
Circumference and Area of Circles, 5-7
Effects of Changing Lengths, 6-8
Measurement of Prisms, Pyramids, Cylinders, and Cones, 6-8
Measurement of Rectangular Solids, 5-7
Perimeter and Area of Rectangles, 4-6
The Pythagorean Relationship, 6-8

Spanish Edition
Constructores II: Ingeniería Creativa Con Construcciones
    LEGO®, 4-9
    The entire book is written in Spanish. English pages not included.

* Spanish supplements are available for these books. They are only
  available as downloads from the AIMS website. The supplements
  contain only the student pages in Spanish; you will need the English
  version of the book for the teacher's text.

For further information, contact:
AIMS Education Foundation • P.O. Box 8120 • Fresno, California 93747-8120
www.aimsedu.org • 559.255.6396 (fax) • 888.733.2467 (toll free)

Duplication Rights

No part of any AIMS books, magazines, activities, or content—digital or otherwise—may be reproduced or transmitted in any form or by any means—including photocopying, taping, or information storage/retrieval systems—except as noted below.

Standard Duplication Rights

- A person or school purchasing AIMS activities (in books, magazines, or in digital form) is hereby granted permission to make up to 200 copies of any portion of those activities, provided these copies will be used for educational purposes and only at one school site.
- Workshop or conference presenters may make one copy of any portion of a purchased activity for each participant, with a limit of five activities per workshop or conference session.
- All copies must bear the AIMS Education Foundation copyright information.

Standard duplication rights apply to activities received at workshops, free sample activities provided by AIMS, and activities received by conference participants.

Unlimited Duplication Rights

Unlimited duplication rights may be purchased in cases where AIMS users wish to:
- make more than 200 copies of a book/magazine/activity,
- use a book/magazine/activity at more than one school site, or
- make an activity available on the Internet (see below).

These rights permit unlimited duplication of purchased books, magazines, and/or activities (including revisions) for use at a given school site.

Activities received at workshops are eligible for upgrade from standard to unlimited duplication rights.

Free sample activities and activities received as a conference participant are not eligible for upgrade from standard to unlimited duplication rights.

State-Specific Science modules are licensed to one classroom/one teacher and are therefore not eligible for upgrade from standard to unlimited duplication rights.

Upgrade Fees

The fees for upgrading from standard to unlimited duplication rights are:
- $5 per activity per site,
- $25 per book per site, and
- $10 per magazine issue per site.

The cost of upgrading is shown in the following examples:
- activity: 5 activities x 5 sites x $5 = $125
- book: 10 books x 5 sites x $25 = $1250
- magazine issue: 1 issue x 5 sites x $10 = $50

Purchasing Unlimited Duplication Rights

To purchase unlimited duplication rights, please provide us the following:
1. The name of the individual responsible for coordinating the purchase of duplication rights.
2. The title of each book, activity, and magazine issue to be covered.
3. The number of school sites and name of each site for which rights are being purchased.
4. Payment (check, purchase order, credit card)

Requested duplication rights are automatically authorized with payment. The individual responsible for coordinating the purchase of duplication rights will be sent a certificate verifying the purchase.

Internet Use

AIMS materials may be made available on the Internet if all of the following stipulations are met:
1. The materials to be put online are purchased as PDF files from AIMS (i.e., no scanned copies).
2. Unlimited duplication rights are purchased for all materials to be put online for each school at which they will be used. (See above.)
3. The materials are made available via a secure, password-protected system that can only be accessed by employees at schools for which duplication rights have been purchased.

AIMS materials may not be made available on any publicly accessible Internet site.